S0-AQH-742

END-OF-YEAR RESOURCES

Review Projects

Getting Ready for Grade 6

These lessons review prerequisite skills and prepare for next year's content.

CORRELATIONS

It's Common Core Math

GO Math! for Kindergarten-Grade 6 combines powerful teaching strategies with never-before-seen components to offer everything needed to successfully teach and learn the Common Core State Standards.

Houghton Mifflin Harcourt

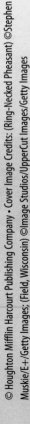

Copyright © 2015 by Houghton Mifflin Harcourt Publishing Company

Printed in the U.S.A.

ISBN 978-0-544-29344-1

8 9 10 11 12 13 14   0029   23 22 21 20 19 18 17 16
4500602363   C D E F G

Table of Contents

PROGRAM OVERVIEW

About *GO Math!*

Planning Resources

that's perfect for 21st century students.

In the **GO Math!** classroom, teachers and students can choose a print-based approach, an online approach, or a blended learning approach. In each case, the focus is on the major work of the grade. The **GO Math!** team of authors carefully developed a coherent K–12 progression to help students connect concepts across and within grade levels. Whether you choose print or digital pathways, you'll find the rigor required for success with the Common Core.

Math on the Spot videos, available for every lesson in GO Math!, support teachers and students, within the classroom and at home.

3-Digit Number	1-Digit Number	Sum	Product
213	4	217	852
214	3	217	642
215	2	217	
216	1	217	

A way of thinking about learning

GO Math! helps students engage with the standards and practices in new ways. Lessons begin with problem-based situations and then build to more abstract problems. All along the way, students use multiple models, manipulatives, quick pictures, and symbols to build mathematical understanding. Best of all, **GO Math!** is write-in at every grade level, so students are completely engaged.

GO Math! reflects what is at the heart of the Common Core Standards,

FOCUS   COHERENCE   RIGOR

that truly prepares students for the Common Core Assessments.

GO Math! works! Using manipulatives, multiple models, and rich, rigorous questions, students move through a carefully-sequenced arc of learning. They develop deep conceptual understanding, and then they practice, apply, and discuss what they know with skill and confidence. The equal emphases on understanding, procedural skills and fluency, and application help turn students into problem solvers and critical thinkers.

Digital resources to help personalize learning for students . . .

The Interactive Student Edition offers an alternate way to access grade-level content with audio, video, and animation. Our unique Personal Math Trainer® Powered by Knewton™ is embedded in the Interactive Student Edition to support students as they develop understanding. The Personal Math Trainer is a state-of-the-art, adaptive assessment and intervention system. In this tablet-based, mobile, and online environment, students receive a completely-personalized learning experience, focused on in-depth understanding, fluency, and application of standards.

and the HMH Player app to help teachers with planning, instruction, and collaboration.

With the HMH Player app, teachers and students can access the Interactive Student Edition while connected to the Internet from tablets, laptops, or desktop computers. They can download Personal Math Trainer assignments and content to their devices for offline access at any time. In addition, HMH Player includes powerful presentation tools for teachers and collaboration tools that keep teachers and students connected.

Create daily lesson plans with a single search.

Works in both online and offline environments.

Organize resources quickly.

See a snapshot of recent student report data.

Reports

Class Assignments | Class Progress

Mr. Ryan's Class

Class Standards Progress

82%

Key
90%-100%
80%-89%
70%-79%
60%-69%
0%-59%

Student Name ▾	Average
Grace, Emma	76%
Guerra, Devin	91%
Hannon, Erin	95%
Plato, Kacy	89%
Risner, Ellie	91%

84% — 2.OA.C.3 National Common Core Math (2013)
90% — 2.NBT.A.2 National Common Core Math (2013)
91% — 2.NBT.A.3 National Common Core Math (2013)
81% — 2.NBT.B.5 National Common Core Math (2013)
67% — 2.NBT.B.6 National Common Core Math (2013)

Grab-and-Go Resources,

GO Math! works for the busy teacher. Everything from Teacher Editions to activity centers to manipulatives are organized in a ready-made, grab-and-go way to save you time.

GO Math! Teacher Editions are color-coded by Critical Area and organized by chapter to help teachers quickly identify materials and flexibly organize their curriculum. In addition, color coding is used to identify content as major, supporting, or additional work, providing teachers with a simple system to quickly identify and emphasize the most important grade-level material. The **GO Math!** classroom focuses on developing in-depth understanding and fosters communication within an engaging, inclusive environment.

perfect for the busy teacher.

The Grab-and-Go Differentiated Centers Kits are ready-made differentiated math centers with activities, games, and literature. Resources for every lesson and special challenge materials make the Grab-and-Go Kits the perfect resource for independent practice.

Digital Resources

FOR LEARNING. . .

 Interactive Student Edition

- Immerses students in an interactive, multi-sensory math environment
- Enhances learning with scaffolded, interactive instruction and just-in-time feedback
- Provides audio reinforcement for each lesson
- Makes learning a two-way experience, using a variety of interactive tools

FOR ASSESSMENT AND INTERVENTION. . .

 Personal Math Trainer

- Creates a personalized learning path for each student
- Provides opportunities for practice, homework, and assessment
- Includes worked-out examples and helpful video support
- Offers targeted intervention and extra support to build proficiency and understanding

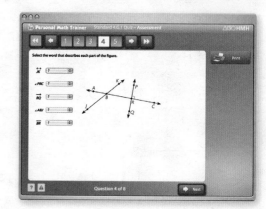

FOR DAILY MATH TUTORING. . .

 Math on the Spot Videos

- Models good problem-solving thinking in every lesson
- Engages students through interesting animations and fun characters
- Builds student problem-solving proficiency and confidence
- Builds the skills needed for success on the Common Core Assessments

FOR SIMPLICITY...

HMH Player App

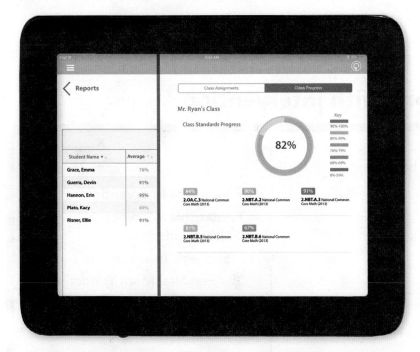

It's For Students ...

- Content is available online, offline, and on-the-go!
- Students are engaged in class, at home, and anywhere in between for uninterrupted instruction
- Raise a Hand for instant student-teacher-student communication

... And For Teachers!

- Teachers can monitor student progress in real time
- Lesson customization features allow teachers to deliver personalized learning
- Plan your lessons, make assignments, and view results from the convenience of your classroom, at home, or on-the-go
- Supports blended learning through anywhere digital instruction

FOR TEACHING...

Digital Management System

- Manage online all program content and components
- Search for and select resources based on Common Core State Standards
- Identify resources based on student ability and needs
- View and assign student lessons, practice, assessments, and more

Professional Development Videos

- Learn more about the Common Core and Common Core content
- See first-hand the integration of the Mathematical Practices
- Watch students engaged in a productive struggle

Assessment ➡ Diagnosis ➡ Intervention

Data-Driven Decision Making

GO Math! allows for quick and accurate data-driven decision making so you can spend more instructional time tailored to students' needs.

Program Assessment Options with Intervention

Diagnostic

To allow students to be engaged from the beginning of the year

- **Prerequisite Skills Inventory** in *Chapter Resources*
- **Beginning-of-Year Test** in *Chapter Resources*
- **Show What You Know** in *Student Edition*

 **RtI**

- Intensive Intervention
- Intensive Intervention User Guide
- Strategic Intervention
- Personal Math Trainer

Formative

To monitor students' understanding of lessons and to adjust instruction accordingly

- **Lesson Quick Check** in *Teacher Edition*
- **Lesson Practice** in *Student Edition*
- **Mid-Chapter Checkpoint** in *Student Edition*
- **Portfolio** in *Chapter Resources* and *Teacher Edition*
- **Middle-of-Year Test** in *Chapter Resources*

 **RtI**

- **Reteach** with each lesson
- **RtI: Tier 1 and Tier 2 Activities** online
- Personal Math Trainer

Summative

To determine whether students have achieved the chapter objectives

- **Chapter Review/Test** in *Student Edition*
- **Chapter Test** in *Chapter Resources* (Common Core Assessment format tests)
- **Performance Assessment Task** in *Chapter Resources*
- **End-of-Year Test** in *Chapter Resources*
- **Getting Ready for Grade 6 Test** in *Getting Ready Lessons and Resources*

 **RtI**

- **Reteach** with each lesson
- **RtI: Tier 1 and Tier 2 Activities** online
- Personal Math Trainer

Tracking Yearly Progress

Beginning of the Year

Beginning-of-Year Test determines how many of this year's Common Core State Standards students already understand. Adjust lesson pacing for skills that need light coverage and allow more time for skills students find challenging.

During the Year

Chapter Tests, Performance Assessments, and the Middle-of-Year Test monitor students' progress throughout the year. Plan time to reinforce skills students have not mastered.

End of the Year

End-of-Year Test assesses students' mastery of this year's Common Core State Standards. Reinforce skills that students find challenging in order to provide the greatest possible success.

Performance Assessment

Performance Assessment helps to reveal the thinking strategies students use to solve problems. The Performance Tasks in *GO Math!* can be used to complete the picture for how students reason about mathematics.

GO Math! has a Performance Task for each Chapter and Critical Area. Each task has several parts that target specific math concepts, skills, and strategies. These tasks can help assess students' ability to use what they have learned to solve everyday problems. Teachers can plan for students to complete one task at a time or use an extended amount of time to complete the entire assessment. Projects for each Critical Area also serve to assess students' problem solving strategies and understanding of mathematical concepts they learn in the Critical Area.

Augmenting the Performance Tasks are a series of professional development videos featuring author Juli Dixon. Working with students, Juli models effective teaching and assessment practices. Additionally, each video provides insight into the dynamics of the classroom and how to use tasks not only to assess progress, but also to deepen understanding.

The Performance Tasks and Critical Area Projects offer the following features:

- They model good instruction.
- They are flexible.
- They are diagnostic.
- They use authentic instruction.
- They encourage the thinking process.
- They are scored holistically.

✓ *GO Math! Personal Math Trainer*® *Powered by Knewton*™

- Online and adaptive homework, assessment, practice, and intervention engine
- Algorithmic, tech-enhanced items with wrong-answer feedback and learning aids
- Pre-built assignments that can generate personalized warm-ups, enrichment, or intervention

Authors

Edward B. Burger, Ph.D.
President, Southwestern University
Georgetown, Texas

Juli K. Dixon, Ph.D.
Professor, Mathematics Education
University of Central Florida
Orlando, Florida

Matthew R. Larson, Ph.D.
K-12 Curriculum Specialist for Mathematics
Lincoln Public Schools
Lincoln, Nebraska

Martha E. Sandoval-Martinez
Math Instructor
El Camino College
Torrance, California

Steven J. Leinwand
Principal Research Analyst
American Institutes for Research (AIR)
Washington, D.C.

Contributor and Consultant

Rena Petrello
Professor, Mathematics
Moorpark College
Moorpark, CA

Elizabeth Jiménez
CEO, GEMAS Consulting
Professional Expert on English Learner Education
Bilingual Education and Dual Language
Pomona, California

GO Math! Reviewers and Field Test Teachers

Janine L. Ambrose
Instructional Coach
Grades Taught: K–7
Sunset Ridge Elementary
Pendergast Elementary School District
Phoenix, Arizona

Patricia R. Barbour
Teacher: Grade 2
Sara Lindemuth Primary School
Susquehanna Township School District
Harrisburg, Pennsylvania

Pamela Bauer
Speech/Language Pathologist, M.A., CCC/SLP
Special School District of St. Louis County
Kindergarten Interventionist
Arrowpoint Elementary
Hazelwood, Missouri

James Brohn
Principal
Morning Star Lutheran School
Jackson, Wisconsin

Earl S. Brown
Teacher: Middle School Math
Susquehanna Township Middle School
Susquehanna Township School District
Harrisburg, Pennsylvania

Rebecca Centerino
Teacher: Grade 1
Zitzman Elementary
Meramec Valley RIII School District
Pacific, Missouri

Jessica Z. Jacobs
Assistant Principal
Thomas Holtzman Junior Elementary School
Susquehanna Township School District
Harrisburg, Pennsylvania

Tonya Leonard
Teacher: Grade 3
Peine Ridge Elementary
Wentzville RIV School District
Wentzville, Missouri

Jennifer Love Frier
Teacher: Grade 1
Olathe School District
Olathe, Kansas

Michelle Mieger
Teacher: Grade 3
Cedar Springs Elementary
Northwest R-1
House Springs, Missouri

Jeanne K. Selissen
Teacher: Grade 4
Tewksbury School District
Tewksbury, Massachusetts

Jo Ellen Showers
Teacher: Grade K
Sara Lindemuth Primary School
Susquehanna Township School District
Harrisburg, Pennsylvania

Judith M. Stagoski
Grades Taught: 5–8
District: Archdiocese of St. Louis
St. Louis, Missouri

Pauline Von Hoffer
Grades Taught: 4–12
Curriculum Coordinator
Wentzville School District
Wentzville, Missouri

© Houghton Mifflin Harcourt Publishing Company • Image Credits: (bg) Photodisc/Getty Images

Common Core State Standards for Mathematics

Content Standards

PROFESSIONAL DEVELOPMENT

by Matthew R. Larson, Ph.D.
K–12 Curriculum Specialist for Mathematics
Lincoln Public Schools
Lincoln, Nebraska

Why Common Core State Standards for Mathematics?

The Common Core State Standards Initiative was a state-led process initiated by the Council of Chief State School Officers (CCSSO) and The National Governors Association (NGA). The goal was to create a set of Career and College Readiness Standards in mathematics (and English/Language Arts) so that all students graduate from high school ready for college and/or work. The K–8 standards outline a grade-by-grade roadmap to prepare students for the Career and College Readiness Standards.

Two primary concerns motivated the Common Core State Standards Initiative. First, inconsistent curricular standards, assessments, and proficiency cut scores across the 50 states raised equity issues (Reed, 2009). These different systems often led to wide disparities between student scores on state assessments in reading and math compared to student performance on the National Assessment of Educational Progress (Schneider, 2007). Second, U.S. students are not leaving school with skills necessary for success in college or the workforce. Results of international assessments, including *PISA* (Baldi, Jin, Skemer, Green, & Herget, 2007) and *TIMSS* (Gonzales, Williams, Jocelyn, Roey, Kastberg, & Brenwald, 2008) indicate that U.S. students do not achieve in mathematics at the level of students in other countries. This raises concern about U.S. economic competitiveness in an environment where U.S. students compete with students all across the globe.

Organization of the Common Core State Standards for Mathematics

The *Common Core State Standards for Mathematics* are organized into content standards and standards for mathematical practice. The content standards are addressed in this article.

The content standards have three levels of organization. The standards define what students should understand and be able to do. These standards are organized into clusters of related standards to emphasize mathematical connections. Finally, domains represent larger groups of related standards. The development and grade placement of standards considered research-based learning progressions with respect to how students' mathematical knowledge develops over time. At the elementary (K–6) level, there are ten content domains. Each grade addresses four or five domains.

Domain	Grade Level
Counting and Cardinality	K
Operations and Algebraic Thinking	K, 1, 2, 3, 4, 5
Number and Operations in Base Ten	K, 1, 2, 3, 4, 5
Measurement and Data	K, 1, 2, 3, 4, 5
Geometry	K, 1, 2, 3, 4, 5, 6
Number and Operations—Fractions	3, 4, 5
Ratios and Proportional Relationships	6
The Number System	6
Expressions and Equations	6
Statistics and Probability	6

Within each grade, each cluster (and the standards within each cluster) is considered to represent the major work of the grade, supplemental work, or additional work. Within the *Planning and Pacing Guide Instructional Path* in this *Planning Guide*, each lesson is color-coded to indicate whether the lesson is addressing the major work, the content that is supplemental, or the content that is additional.

While the total number of standards in the *Common Core* is generally less than the number of standards in many current state standard documents (NCTM, 2005; Reys, Chval, Dingman, McNaught, Regis, & Togashi, 2007), the emphasis in the *Common Core* is not simply on a list with fewer standards, but on a list that is also more specific and clear.

Note: This article references *Common Core State Standards for Mathematics.* © Copyright 2010.
National Governors Association Center for Best Practices and Council of Chief State School Officers. All rights reserved.

Critical Areas

The *Common Core* also specifies critical areas for instructional emphasis at each grade level. These areas are shown below.

K	• Representing, relating, and operating on whole numbers initially with sets of objects • Describing shapes and space
1	• Developing understanding of addition, subtraction, and strategies for addition and subtraction within 20 • Developing understanding of whole number relationships and place value, including grouping in tens and ones • Developing understanding of linear measurement and measuring lengths as iterating length units • Reasoning about attributes of, and composing and decomposing geometric shapes
2	• Extending understanding of base-ten notation • Building fluency with addition and subtraction • Using standard units of measure • Describing and analyzing shapes
3	• Developing understanding of multiplication and division and strategies for multiplication and division within 100 • Developing understanding of fractions, especially unit fractions • Developing understanding of the structure of rectangular arrays and of area • Describing and analyzing two-dimensional shapes

4	• Developing understanding and fluency with multi-digit multiplication, and developing understanding of dividing to find quotients involving multi-digit dividends • Developing an understanding of fraction equivalence, addition and subtraction of fractions with like denominators, and multiplication of fractions by whole numbers • Understanding that geometric figures can be analyzed and classified based on their properties, such as having parallel sides, perpendicular sides, particular angle measures, and symmetry
5	• Developing fluency with addition and subtraction of fractions, and developing understanding of the multiplication of fractions and of division of fractions in limited cases (unit fractions divided by whole numbers and whole numbers divided by unit fractions) • Extending division to 2-digit divisors, integrating decimal fractions into the place value system and developing understanding of operations with decimals to hundredths, and developing fluency with whole number and decimal operations • Developing understanding of volume.
6	• Connecting ratio and rate to whole number multiplication and division and using concepts of ratio and rate to solve problems • Completing understanding of division of fractions and extending the notion of number to the system of rational numbers, which includes negative numbers • Writing, interpreting, and using expressions and equations • Developing understanding of statistical thinking

This design permits instruction in each grade to focus on fewer concepts and skills in greater depth, while simultaneously building a foundation for the next grade. For example, in the *Common Core,* fractions are not a significant focus of the curriculum until third grade; although, students decompose two-dimensional figures in previous grades to develop a foundation for fractions in third grade. Similarly, probability is delayed until the middle grades in the *Common Core.*

The *Common Core* states that "mathematical understanding and procedural skill are equally important," but stresses conceptual understanding of key ideas and organizing principles, to structure essential big ideas. Similar to other recent recommendations (NCTM, 2000; NMAP, 2008), this emphasis on conceptual understanding and procedural skill, along with the standards for mathematical practice calls for a balanced approach to mathematics instruction and the curriculum.

Common Core State Standards for Mathematics and *GO Math!*

Nearly all content standards today, whether articulated by a state, NCTM, or the *Common Core,* share one thing in common: they call for a more focused and coherent curriculum that treats topics in a manner that will enable students to develop deep understanding of the content. *GO Math!* espouses this emphasis on a focused and coherent curriculum that teaches for depth of understanding to help students learn.

All standards documents share one additional feature: alone they are not enough to ensure that students

achieve at higher levels (Fuhrman, Resnick, & Shepard, 2009). In *GO Math!*, the *Common Core State Standards* are merely the starting point. *GO Math!* represents a comprehensive system of mathematics instruction that provides teachers the tools they need to help students succeed with more focused and rigorous mathematics standards. Research-based *GO Math!* includes multiple instructional approaches, diagnostic assessments linked to differentiated instructional resources and tiered interventions, along with technology solutions to support and motivate students.

Standards for Mathematical Practice

PROFESSIONAL DEVELOPMENT **by Juli K. Dixon, Ph.D.**
Professor, Mathematics Education
University of Central Florida
Orlando, Florida

Developing Processes and Proficiencies in Mathematics Learners

There are eight mathematical practices. They are based on the National Council of Teachers of Mathematics' (NCTM) Process Standards (NCTM, 2000) and the National Research Council's (NRC) Strands of Mathematical Proficiency (NRC, 2001).

It is likely that good teachers can find evidence of each of these standards for mathematical practice in their current teaching. Regardless, it is useful to examine them and think about how each contributes to the development of mathematically proficient students.

Throughout *GO Math!*, the Mathematical Practices incorporated within a lesson are identified in the Student Edition and the Teacher Edition. In some instances, a lesson will focus on a part of a practice—this approach will break apart the standard in such a way as to support in-depth understanding of the practice and over time will aid students in attending to the full meaning of the practice.

What follows is a description of how they might look in an elementary school classroom. Each of these examples is reflective of experiences supported by *GO Math!*

GO Math! supports the Standards for Mathematical Practice through several specific features including:

- Lessons focused on depth of content knowledge
- Unlock the Problem sections to begin lessons
- Math Talk questions prompting students to use varied strategies and to explain their reasoning
- Explicit use of specific practices within a lesson, with accompanying point-of-use teacher support
- Support for manipulative use and drawings directly on the student pages
- Prompts that lead students to write their own problems or to determine if the reasoning of others is reasonable
- Real-world problems that encourage students to develop productive dispositions

Practice 1: Make sense of problems and persevere in solving them.

This practice brings to mind developing a productive disposition as described in *Adding It Up* (NRC, 2001). In order for students to develop the diligence intended with this practice, they must be provided with problems for which a pathway toward a solution is not immediately evident. If students are asked to determine how much of a cookie each person would receive if 4 cookies were shared among 5 people, a solution pathway is evident if students understand fractions. The students could simply divide each cookie into five equal pieces and give each person one fifth of each cookie or $\frac{4}{5}$ of a cookie in all. Now, consider the same problem given the constraint that the first three cookies are each broken into two equal pieces to start and each person is given half of a cookie.

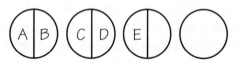

The problem is now more interesting and challenging. How will the remaining pieces of cookies be distributed among the five people? How will the students determine how much of a cookie each person has in all when all the cookies are shared? The students will likely refer back to the context of the problem to make sense of how to solve it, they will also very likely use pictures in their solution process. A solution is within reach but it will require diligence to persevere in reaching it.

Practice 2: Reason abstractly and quantitatively.

Story problems provide important opportunities for young learners to make sense of mathematics around them. Students often use strategies including acting out the problem to make sense of a solution path. Another important strategy is for students to make sense of the problem situation by determining a number sentence that could represent the problem and then solving it in a mathematically proficient way. Consider the following problem: *Jessica has 7 key chains in her collection. How many more does she need to have 15 key chains all together?*

A child is presented with this problem, but rather than focusing on key words, the child uses the story to make sense of a solution process. The child knows to start with 7 then add something to that to get 15. The child represents this story abstractly by writing $7 + \underline{} = 15$. Then the child reasons quantitatively by thinking $7 + 3 = 10$ and $10 + 5 = 15$ so $7 + 8$ must equal 15 (because 3 and 5 are 8). The child then returns to the problem to see if a solution of 8 key chains makes sense. In doing so, the child makes "sense of quantities and their relationships in problem situations" (NGA Center/CCSSO, 2010, p. 6).

Practice 3: Construct viable arguments and critique the reasoning of others.

Students need to explain and justify their solution strategies. They should also listen to the explanations of other students and try to make sense of them. They will then be able to incorporate the reasoning of others into their own strategies and improve upon their own solutions. An example of this follows.

A group of students explores formulas for areas of quadrilaterals. Students make sense of the formula for the area of a parallelogram as $b \times h$ by decomposing parallelograms and composing a rectangle with the same area. Following this exploration, a student conjectures that the formula for the area of the trapezoid is also $b \times h$. The student draws this picture and says that the trapezoid can be "turned into" a rectangle with the same base by "moving one triangle over to the other side."

This student has constructed a viable argument based on a special type of trapezoid. Another student agrees that this formula works for an isosceles trapezoid

but asks if it will also work for a general trapezoid. This second student has made sense of the reasoning of the first student and asked a question to help improve the argument.

Practice 4: Model with mathematics.

Children need opportunities to use mathematics to solve real-world problems. As students learn more mathematics, the ways they model situations with mathematics should become more efficient. Consider the problem: *Riley has 4 blue erasers, Alex has 4 yellow erasers, and Paige has 4 purple erasers. How many erasers do they have in all?* A young child would likely model this problem with $4 + 4 + 4$. However, a mathematically proficient student in third grade should model the same situation with 3×4. This demonstrates how modeling will evolve through a child's experiences in mathematics and will change as their understanding grows.

A useful strategy for making sense of mathematics is for students to develop real-life contexts to correspond to mathematical expressions. This supports the reflexive relationship that if a student can write a word problem for a given expression, then the student can model a similar word problem with mathematics. Consider $\frac{4}{5} - \frac{1}{2}$. If a student is able to create a word problem to support this fraction subtraction, then, given a word problem, the student is more likely to be able to model the word problem with mathematics and solve it.

Practice 5: Use appropriate tools strategically.

At first glance, one might think that this practice refers to technological tools exclusively, however, tools also include paper and pencil, number lines and manipulatives (or concrete models). Mathematically proficient students are able to determine which tool to use for a given task. An example to illustrate this practice involves multiplying fractions. A student might choose to use a number line for one problem and paper and pencil procedures for another. If presented the problem $\frac{1}{3} \times \frac{3}{4}$, a mathematically proficient student might draw a number line and divide the distance from 0 to 1 into 4 equal parts drawing a darker line through the first three fourths. That student would see that $\frac{1}{3}$ of the $\frac{3}{4}$ is $\frac{1}{4}$ of the whole.

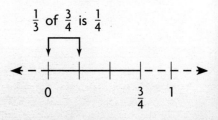

However, the same student presented with the problem $\frac{1}{3} \times \frac{4}{7}$ might not use a drawing at all but might find it more efficient to multiply the numerators and the denominators of the factors to get $\frac{4}{21}$ as the product. Both solution paths illustrate strategic use of tools for the given problems.

Practice 6: Attend to precision.

An important aspect of precision in mathematics is developed through the language used to describe it. This can be illustrated with definitions of geometric shapes. A kindergarten child is not expected to classify quadrilaterals. However, it is appropriate for a kindergarten child to name and describe shapes including squares and rectangles. Teachers seeking to support kindergarten children to attend to precision will include squares within sets of other rectangles so that these children will not use the language that all rectangles have two long sides and two short sides. These same students will be more likely to be able to correctly classify squares and rectangles in third grade because of this attention to precision when they are in kindergarten.

Practice 7: Look for and make use of structure.

Students who have made sense of strategies based on properties for finding products of single digit factors (basic facts) will be more likely to apply those properties when exploring multidigit multiplication. Consider the importance of the distributive property in looking for and making use of structure in this case. A student who has made sense of 6×7 by solving 6×5 and 6×2 has used a strategy based on the distributive property where 6×7 can be thought of as $6 \times (5 + 2)$ and then the 6 can be "distributed over" the 5 and 2. This same student can apply the distributive property to make sense of 12×24 by thinking of 24 as $20 + 4$ and solving $12 \times 20 + 12 \times 4$. A student who can make sense of multidigit multiplication in this way is on a good path to making sense of the structure of the standard algorithm for multidigit multiplication.

Practice 8: Look for and express regularity in repeated reasoning.

Whether performing simple calculations or solving complex problems, students should take advantage of the regularity of mathematics. If students who are exploring the volume of right rectangular prisms are given centimeter cubes and grid paper, they can build a prism with a given base and explore how the volume changes as the height of the prism increases. Students who look for ways to describe the change should see that the height of the prism is a factor of the volume of the prism and that if the area of the base is known, the volume of the prism is determined by multiplying the area of the base by the height of the prism. Identifying this pattern and repeated reasoning will help students build an understanding of the formula for the volume of right rectangular prisms.

As evidenced by the examples of mathematical practices in elementary school classrooms, "a lack of understanding effectively prevents a student from engaging in the mathematical practices" (NGA Center/CCSSO, 2010, p. 8). Teachers address this challenge by focusing on mathematical practices while developing an understanding of the content they support. In so doing, this process facilitates the development of mathematically proficient students.

Supporting Mathematical Practices Through Questioning

When you ask...	*Students...*
• What is the problem asking? • How will you use that information? • What other information do you need? • Why did you choose that operation? • What is another way to solve that problem? • What did you do first? Why? • What can you do if you don't know how to solve a problem? • Have you solved a problem similar to this one? • When did you realize your first method would not work for this problem? • How do you know your answer makes sense?	**MP1** Make sense of problems and persevere in solving them.
• What is a situation that could be represented by this equation? • What operation did you use to represent the situation? • Why does that operation represent the situation? • What properties did you use to find the answer? • How do you know your answer is reasonable?	**MP2** Reason abstractly and quantitatively.
• Will that method always work? • How do you know? • What do you think about what she said? • Who can tell us about a different method? • What do you think will happen if...? • When would that not be true? • Why do you agree/disagree with what he said? • What do you want to ask her about that method? • How does that drawing support your work?	**MP3** Construct viable arguments and critique the reasoning of others.
• Why is that a good model for this problem? • How can you use a simpler problem to help you find the answer? • What conclusions can you make from your model? • How would you change your model if...?	**MP4** Model with mathematics.
• What could you use to help you solve the problem? • What strategy could you use to make that calculation easier? • How would estimation help you solve that problem? • Why did you decide to use...?	**MP5** Use appropriate tools strategically.
• How do you know your answer is reasonable? • How can you use math vocabulary in your explanation? • How do you know those answers are equivalent? • What does that mean?	**MP6** Attend to precision.
• How did you discover that pattern? • What other patterns can you find? • What rule did you use to make this group? • Why can you use that property in this problem? • How is that like...?	**MP7** Look for and make use of structure.
• What do you remember about...? • What happens when...? • What if you... instead of...? • What might be a shortcut for...?	**MP8** Look for and express regularity in repeated reasoning.

For the full text of the Standards for Mathematical Practices, see *Mathematical Practices in GO Math!* in the *Planning Guide*.

STANDARDS FOR MATHEMATICAL PRACTICES
Mathematical Practices in *GO Math!*

Mathematical Practices	Throughout *GO Math!* Look for...	Explanation
1. Make sense of problems and persevere in solving them. Mathematically proficient students start by explaining to themselves the meaning of a problem and looking for entry points to its solution. They analyze givens, constraints, relationships, and goals. They make conjectures about the form and meaning of the solution and plan a solution pathway rather than simply jumping into a solution attempt. They consider analogous problems, and try special cases and simpler forms of the original problem in order to gain insight into its solution. They monitor and evaluate their progress and change course if necessary. Older students might, depending on the context of the problem, transform algebraic expressions or change the viewing window on their graphing calculator to get the information they need. Mathematically proficient students can explain correspondences between equations, verbal descriptions, tables, and graphs or draw diagrams of important features and relationships, graph data, and search for regularity or trends. Younger students might rely on using concrete objects or pictures to help conceptualize and solve a problem. Mathematically proficient students check their answers to problems using a different method, and they continually ask themselves, "Does this make sense?" They can understand the approaches of others to solving complex problems and identify correspondences between different approaches.	**Some Examples:** **Problem Solving Lessons** Grade 3, Lesson 7.10 Grade 4, Lesson 4.12 Grade 5, Lesson 1.9 Grade 6, Lesson 6.5 **Unlock the Problem** Grade 3, Lesson 3.3 Grade 4, Lesson 2.1 Grade 5, Lesson 2.6 Grade 6, Lesson 2.9 **About the Math** Grade 3, Lesson 2.6 Grade 4, Lesson 13.5 Grade 5, Lesson 2.7 Grade 6, Lesson 9.3	**Students learn to:** • analyze a problem to determine relationships. • explain what information they need to find to solve the problem. • determine what information they need to use to solve the problem. • develop a plan for solving the problem. • use concrete objects to conceptualize a problem. • draw diagrams to help solve problems. • evaluate the solution for reasonableness.
	One Way/Another Way Grade 3, Lesson 4.8 Grade 4, Lesson 13.3 Grade 5, Lesson 6.3 Grade 6, Lessons 1.2, 5.6 **Try Another Problem** Grade 3, Lesson 5.3 Grade 4, Lesson 9.5 Grade 5, Lesson 1.9 Grade 6, Lesson 4.4 **Share and Show** Grade 3, Lesson 4.10 Grade 4, Lesson 5.3 Grade 5, Lesson 2.9 Grade 6, Lesson 5.5	**Students learn to:** • use different approaches to solving a problem and identify how the approaches are alike and how they are different. • look at analogous problems and apply techniques used in the original problem to gain insight into the solution of a new problem.
	Check your answer. Is your answer reasonable? Estimate to check your answer. Grade 3, Lesson 1.10 Grade 4, Lesson 2.4 Grade 5, Lessons 2.1–2.2 Grade 6, Lesson 1.1	**Students learn to:** • develop different methods of checking their answers, such as using inverse operations or estimation using rounding. • use critical thinking to justify why an answer is reasonable and explain the solution process.

Teacher Edition   Student Edition

Mathematical Practices	Throughout *GO Math!* Look for...	Explanation
2. Reason abstractly and quantitatively. Mathematically proficient students make sense of quantities and their relationships in problem situations. They bring two complementary abilities to bear on problems involving quantitative relationships: the ability to *decontextualize*—to abstract a given situation and represent it symbolically and manipulate the representing symbols as if they have a life of their own, without necessarily attending to their referents— and the ability to *contextualize*, to pause as needed during the manipulation process in order to probe into the referents for the symbols involved. Quantitative reasoning entails habits of creating a coherent representation of the problem at hand; considering the units involved; attending to the meaning of quantities, not just how to compute them; and knowing and flexibly using different properties of operations and objects.	**Some Examples:** **Unlock the Problem** Grade 3, Lessons 7.1, 11.7 Grade 4, Lesson 2.2 Grade 5, Lesson 3.3 Grade 6, Lesson 8.2	**Students learn to:** • represent a real-world situation symbolically as an equation. • use a mathematical algorithm to solve a problem and then place the result back into the context of the original situation.
	Measurement and Geometry Lessons Grade 3, Lesson 11.6 Grade 4, Lessons 13.1, 13.2 Grade 5, Lessons 11.7–11.9 Grade 6, Lessons 10.1, 11.2	**Students learn to:** • construct and measure geometric figures by counting and then adding units in a systematic deconstruction of the figure that builds to a comprehensive understanding of a formula.
	Lessons on the properties of operations Grade 3, Lesson 4.9 Grade 4, Lesson 2.8 Grade 5, Lesson 6.10 Grade 6, Lesson 7.3 **Algebra Lessons** Grade 3, Lesson 4.6 Grade 4, Lesson 7.9 Grade 5, Lesson 11.9 Grade 6, Lesson 7.3	**Students learn to:** • abstract a real-world situation and represent it symbolically as an expression or equation, using numbers, operations, and the grouping properties.
	Lessons on modeling with manipulatives and drawings Grade 3, Lesson 6.9 Grade 4, Lesson 2.1 Grade 5, Lesson 7.2 Grade 6, Lesson 5.1	**Students learn to:** • represent real-world situations with concrete and pictorial models. • use the understanding that they have acquired to represent a situation abstractly with symbols and equations.

Teacher Edition   Student Edition

Mathematical Practices	Throughout *GO Math!* Look for...	Explanation
3. Construct viable arguments and critique the reasoning of others. Mathematically proficient students understand and use stated assumptions, definitions, and previously established results in constructing arguments. They make conjectures and build a logical progression of statements to explore the truth of their conjectures. They are able to analyze situations by breaking them into cases, and can recognize and use counterexamples. They justify their conclusions, communicate them to others, and respond to the arguments of others. They reason inductively about data, making plausible arguments that take into account the context from which the data arose. Mathematically proficient students are also able to compare the effectiveness of two plausible arguments, distinguish correct logic or reasoning from that which is flawed, and—if there is a flaw in an argument—explain what it is. Elementary students can construct arguments using concrete referents such as objects, drawings, diagrams, and actions. Such arguments can make sense and be correct, even though they are not generalized or made formal until later grades. Later, students learn to determine domains to which an argument applies. Students at all grades can listen or read the arguments of others, decide whether they make sense, and ask useful questions to clarify or improve the arguments.	**Some Examples:** **Math Talk** Grade 3, Lesson 4.8 Grade 4, Lesson 5.2 Grade 5, Lesson 11.3 Grade 6, Lesson 8.1	**Students learn to:** • use mathematical language to explain lesson concepts and construct arguments. • use deductive reasoning, definitions, and previously proven conclusions to explore the truth of conjectures.
	Vocabulary Builder Grade 3 Grade 4 Grade 5 Grade 6 **Vocabulary Builder** Grade 3 Grade 4 Grade 5 Grade 6 **Developing Math Language** Grade 3 Grade 4 Grade 5 Grade 6	**Students learn to:** • develop, build, and reinforce mathematics vocabulary. • discuss mathematical definitions. • strengthen their abilities to communicate mathematical ideas to others.
	Sense or Nonsense? Grade 3, Lesson 4.7 Grade 4, Lesson 3.3 Grade 5, Lesson 4.6 Grade 6, Lesson 4.8 **What's the Error?** Grade 3, Lesson 9.2 Grade 4, Lesson 4.2 Grade 5, Lesson 4.1 Grade 6, Lesson 2.1 **Think Smarter Problems** Grade 3, Lesson 8.1 Grade 4, Lesson 7.1 Grade 5, Lesson 6.3 Grade 6, Lesson 1.7 **Go Deeper** Grade 3, Lesson 9.2 Grade 4, Lesson 4.2 Grade 5, Lessons 1.9, 7.5 Grade 6, Lesson 10.6	**Students learn to:** • use previously acquired skills, conclusions, and mathematical reasoning to establish whether a statement is true or false. • use modeling, drawings, equations, and written arguments to prove or disprove a given conjecture. • reason inductively about data. • reason about whether the arguments of others make sense.

Teacher Edition   Student Edition

Mathematical Practices	Throughout GO Math! Look for...	Explanation
4. Model with mathematics. Mathematically proficient students can apply the mathematics they know to solve problems arising in everyday life, society, and the workplace. In early grades, this might be as simple as writing an addition equation to describe a situation. In middle grades, a student might apply proportional reasoning to plan a school event or analyze a problem in the community. By high school, a student might use geometry to solve a design problem or use a function to describe how one quantity of interest depends on another. Mathematically proficient students who can apply what they know are comfortable making assumptions and approximations to simplify a complicated situation, realizing that these may need revision later. They are able to identify important quantities in a practical situation and map their relationships using such tools as diagrams, two-way tables, graphs, flowcharts and formulas. They can analyze those relationships mathematically to draw conclusions. They routinely interpret their mathematical results in the context of the situation and reflect on whether the results make sense, possibly improving the model if it has not served its purpose.	**Some Examples:** **Unlock the Problem • Real World** Grade 3, Lesson 3.2 Grade 4, Lesson 6.1 Grade 5, Lesson 7.9 Grade 6, Lesson 12.4 **Investigate Lessons** Grade 3, Lesson 12.9 Grade 4, Lesson 7.1 Grade 5, Lesson 9.3 Grade 6, Lesson 13.3 **Project** Grade 3 Grade 4 Grade 5 Grade 6 **Connect To... Cross-Curricular** Grade 3, Lesson 9.6 Grade 4, Lesson 7.3 Grade 5, Lesson 7.9 Grade 6, Lesson 4.1 **Literature** Grade 3, Lesson 2.1 Grade 4, Lesson 13.1 Grade 5, Lesson 9.2 Grade 6, Lesson 11.1	**Students learn to:** • model in a 'hands-on' approach to analyze problems with: graphs, manipulatives, equations, and other mathematical tools. **Students learn to:** • model and solve real-world problems in Literature, Science, Social Studies, Art, and other disciplines. • appreciate how mathematics influences their lives in ways both large and small.

Teacher Edition   Student Edition

Mathematical Practices	Throughout *GO Math!* Look for…	Explanation
5. Use appropriate tools strategically. Mathematically proficient students consider the available tools when solving a mathematical problem. These tools might include pencil and paper, concrete models, a ruler, a protractor, a calculator, a spreadsheet, a computer algebra system, a statistical package, or dynamic geometry software. Proficient students are sufficiently familiar with tools appropriate for their grade or course to make sound decisions about when each of these tools might be helpful, recognizing both the insight to be gained and their limitations. For example, mathematically proficient high school students analyze graphs of functions and solutions generated using a graphing calculator. They detect possible errors by strategically using estimation and other mathematical knowledge. When making mathematical models, they know that technology can enable them to visualize the results of varying assumptions, explore consequences, and compare predictions with data. Mathematically proficient students at various grade levels are able to identify relevant external mathematical resources, such as digital content located on a website, and use them to pose or solve problems. They are able to use technological tools to explore and deepen their understanding of concepts.	**Some Examples:** **Investigate Lessons with manipulatives** Grade 3, Lesson 9.6 Grade 4, Lesson 4.7 Grade 5, Lesson 6.1 Grade 6, Lesson 8.3	**Students learn to:** • use available tools to analyze problems through a concrete 'hands on' approach.
	Geometry and Measurement Lessons Grade 3, Lesson 10.7 Grade 4, Lesson 11.3 Grade 5, Lesson 11.6 Grade 6, Lesson 10.2	**Students learn to:** • use appropriate tools to enhance and deepen their understanding of measurement and geometry concepts.
	*i*Tools **Animated Math Models** **HMH Mega Math** All student lessons	**Students learn to:** • use technological tools to enhance and deepen their understanding of concepts and explore consequences of varying the data given.
	Modeling feature Grade 3, Lesson 6.6 Grade 4, Lesson 4.6 Grade 5, Lesson 5.2 Grade 6, Lesson 11.3	**Students learn to:** • use concrete models to enable them to visualize problems.
6. Attend to precision. Mathematically proficient students try to communicate precisely to others. They try to use clear definitions in discussion with others and in their own reasoning. They state the meaning of the symbols they choose, including using the equal sign consistently and appropriately. They are careful about specifying units of measure, and labeling axes to clarify the correspondence with quantities in a problem. They calculate accurately and efficiently, express numerical answers with a degree of precision appropriate for the problem context. In the elementary grades, students give carefully formulated explanations to each other. By the time they reach high school they have learned to examine claims and make explicit use of definitions.	**Math Talk** Grade 3, Lesson 12.6 Grade 4, Lesson 5.5 Grade 5, Lesson 5.7 Grade 6, Lesson 3.3	**Students learn to:** • communicate precisely. • use mathematical vocabulary to communicate their ideas and explanations and to justify their thinking and solutions.
	Skill lessons on equations and comparisons (<, >, and =) Grade 3, Lesson 9.4 Grade 4, Lesson 6.6 Grade 5, Lesson 3.3 Grade 6, Lesson 8.9	**Students learn to:** • state the meaning of the symbols they use in mathematical expressions and sentences accurately. • use the equal sign appropriately. • calculate accurately.
	Lessons with labeling (such as *x* and *y* axes tables, units such as inch or meter) Grade 3, Lessons 2.5, 11.9 Grade 4, Lesson 12.11 Grade 5, Lesson 9.2 Grade 6, Lesson 9.4	**Students learn to:** • use correct measurement units to label solutions. • label axes correctly.
	Investigate Lessons with Bloom's Taxonomy questions Grade 3, Lessons 7.11, 11.1 Grade 4, Lesson 2.5 Grade 5, Lesson 3.5 Grade 6, Lesson 8.5	**Students learn to:** • explain mathematical ideas to each other with correctly composed explanations. • discuss results of an activity and clarify misunderstanding if results are different.

Teacher Edition   Student Edition

© Houghton Mifflin Harcourt Publishing Company • Image Credits: (bg) Photodisc/Getty Images

Mathematical Practices	Throughout *GO Math!* Look for...	Explanation
7. Look for and make use of structure. Mathematically proficient students look closely to discern a pattern or structure. Young students, for example, might notice that three and seven more is the same amount as seven and three more, or they may sort a collection of shapes according to how many sides the shapes have. Later, students will see 7×8 equals the well remembered $7 \times 5 + 7 \times 3$, in preparation for learning about the distributive property. In the expression $x^2 + 9x + 14$, older students can see the 14 as 2×7 and the 9 as $2 + 7$. They recognize the significance of an existing line in a geometric figure and can use the strategy of drawing an auxiliary line for solving problems. They also can step back for an overview and shift perspective. They can see complicated things, such as some algebraic expressions, as single objects or as being composed of several objects. For example, they can see $5 - 3(x - y)^2$ as 5 minus a positive number times a square and use that to realize that its value cannot be more than 5 for any real numbers x and y.	**Some Examples:** **Lessons with grouping** Grade 3, Lessons 1.5, 4.7 Grade 4, Lesson 4.6 Grade 5, Lessons 3.6, 10.6 Grade 6, Lesson 7.7 **Algebra Lessons** Grade 3, Lesson 4.4 Grade 4, Lesson 5.6 Grade 5, Lesson 1.4 Grade 6, Lesson 7.8 **Lessons with patterns and sequencing** Grade 3, Lesson 1.1 Grade 4, Lesson 2.3 Grade 5, Lesson 9.6 Grade 6, Lesson 3.1 **Modeling feature** Grade 3, Lesson 5.3 Grade 4, Lesson 2.5 Grade 5, Lesson 1.8 Grade 6, Lesson 7.7	**Students learn to:** • discern patterns as they use the distributive property to solve a problem. • use mathematical vocabulary to communicate their ideas and explanations and to justify their thinking and solutions. • analyze a problem to determine a rule to describe a number pattern.
8. Look for and express regularity in repeated reasoning. Mathematically proficient students notice if calculations are repeated, and look both for general methods and for shortcuts. Upper elementary students might notice when dividing 25 by 11 that they are repeating the same calculations over and over again, and conclude they have a repeating decimal. By paying attention to the calculation of slope as they repeatedly check whether points are on the line through (1, 2) with slope 3, middle school students might abstract the equation $(y - 2)/(x - 1) = 3$. Noticing the regularity in the way terms cancel when expanding $(x - 1)(x + 1)$, $(x - 1)(x^2 + x + 1)$, and $(x - 1)(x^3 + x^2 + x + 1)$ might lead them to the general formula for the sum of a geometric series. As they work to solve a problem, mathematically proficient students maintain oversight of the process, while attending to the details. They continually evaluate the reasonableness of their intermediate results.	**Computation Lessons** Grade 3, Lesson 7.7 Grade 4, Lesson 4.8 Grade 5, Lesson 4.1 Grade 6, Lesson 2.1 **Connect** Grade 3, Lesson 4.6 Grade 4, Lesson 4.11 Grade 5, Lesson 5.7 Grade 6, Lesson 5.3	**Students learn to:** • see the relationship between addition and subtraction and between multiplication and division. • recognize how structure and calculations are repeated as they build and write fractions as decimals and write decimals as fractions. • discover shortcuts for finding sums, differences, products, and quotients of both whole numbers, decimals, and fractions. • discover relationships between patterns on the multiplication charts and equivalent fractions or ratios.

Teacher Edition   Student Edition

PROFESSIONAL DEVELOPMENT

by Matthew R. Larson, Ph.D.
K–12 Curriculum Specialist for Mathematics
Lincoln Public Schools
Lincoln, Nebraska
NCTM President (2016–2018)

The Algebra Progression in *GO Math!* Grades K–8 and the GIMET-QR

Nearly two decades ago, NCTM first articulated the need for algebra to be a significant strand across the K–8 curriculum in *Principles and Standards for School Mathematics* (NCTM, 2000). The importance of algebra in Grades K–8 was reemphasized in the final report of the National Mathematics Advisory Panel (NMAP, 2008). A coherent, rigorous, and sound learning progression in the K–8 mathematics curriculum is necessary to prepare students not only for high school mathematics courses, but also to ensure they leave high school both college and career ready.

The Grade-Level Instructional Materials Evaluation Tool—Quality Review (GIMET-QR) for Grades K–8 was developed to provide educators with a framework for evaluating the quality of instructional materials and choosing materials that are best suited to provide a coherent learning experience. This tool focuses on the clusters and standards along the progression to algebra continuum.

Using the progression documents from the University of Arizona Institute of Mathematics and the Progression to Algebra Continuum from the Common Core, the developers of GIMET-QR developed additional algebra-progression statements for each grade level. These particular statements provide additional specificity and clarity for the reviewers of instructional materials.

This article examines the Houghton Mifflin Harcourt *GO Math!* Grades K–8 program and the extent to which it reflects and embodies the GIMET-QR algebra-progression statements.

GO Math! Grades K–2

The GIMET-QR algebra-progression statements in this grade span draw from the Common Core domains Counting and Cardinality, Operations and Algebraic Thinking, Number and Operations in Base Ten, and Measurement and Data.

Based on the explanations, diagrams, pictorial representations, and assignments in the *GO Math!* instructional materials, and when considered in the context of the algebra-progression statements, *GO Math!* K–2 is exceptional in its comprehensive approach to algebra preparedness as defined by the GIMET-QR.

Kindergarten

In **Kindergarten**, students represent numbers in multiple ways, including with counters, drawings, and written numerals. Students show how to count objects arranged in lines and in more difficult arrangements. Teacher narrative ensures that students count each object only once and make single counting paths through scattered displays. The logical structure of *GO Math!* counting lessons supports students' understanding that each successive number name in a counting array refers to a quantity that is one greater. When students compare numbers, they do so in a variety of ways, including by using real objects, studying drawings, and counting. The assignments in the Student Edition support these comparisons as well. Lessons offer opportunities for students to match to compare numbers, and they show that one group might look like it has more objects, but matching or counting may yield another result.

It is significant that the Operations and Algebraic Thinking underpinnings for algebra in *GO Math!* at this grade span place notable emphasis on understanding written expressions and equations. Kindergarten students develop the mathematical language of addition and subtraction that is so integral to success with algebra. To solidify this development even more, addition and subtraction situations in *GO Math!* are action oriented, helping students to visualize and understand the change that takes place.

Finally, *GO Math!* Kindergarten is exceptional in its treatment of place value. Students have many hands-on opportunities to compose and decompose numbers as ten ones and some further ones, this concept being a critical step for understanding base-ten notation.

Grade 1

Students in **Grade 1** extend their understanding of algebra ideas in several ways. Students use comparison to represent problem situations, which requires students to conceptualize and represent an unknown. Mathematical language comes into play here as well. *More, fewer, or less* contextual problems can take many forms. *GO Math!* offers extensive opportunities to work toward mastery of the language and contextual complexities. Assignments require students to match objects with drawings and use labels to compare. Later, students use tape diagrams (bar models) as a tool to help them compare. Students represent *compare* situations in different ways, including as unknown-addend problems. Even though students do not use formal properties in their descriptions, they have many opportunities to recognize these properties in action.

In *GO Math!*, emphasis is placed through Math Talk structures on the explanation a student gives for his or her representation of a contextual situation. In *GO Math!* students gain extensive experience with more challenging problem subtypes as they begin developing an algebraic perspective on mathematical situations. *GO Math!* is exceptional in the ways it encourages students to link equations with representations, which leads to a deeper understanding of these precursors to formal algebra.

Here again, *GO Math!* excels in its teaching of place value. Instruction helps students recognize that the digit in the tens place is the critical digit when determining the size of a two-digit number. Assignments require students to explain why this is so. Students connect different strategies: for example, using the relationship between addition and subtraction to explain an unknown-addend problem.

In Grade 1, there are several GIMET-QR statements drawn from the Measurement and Data domain. These include transitive reasoning and the reasoning processes of seriation, conservation, and classification. Both the *GO Math!* recommended teacher instructional narrative and the assignments in the Student Edition emphasize these algebraic building blocks.

Grade 2

Grade 2 students extend their addition and subtraction representations to include two-step problems. *GO Math!* offers a recommended teacher narrative and assignments that engage students in representing two-step problems with equations by using easy subtypes. Students use drawings or combinations of drawings and equations to represent comparison problems or middle-difficulty subtypes. Assignments require students to solve one- and two-step problems that involve adding to, taking from, putting together/taking apart, and comparing and that have unknowns in all positions.

GO Math! offers the instruction and support students need to succeed when reading and writing equations with different placements of the unknown, explaining the different meanings of addition and subtraction, and showing the connection between addition and subtraction equations. Students develop and use mathematical language to explain their reasoning about *result unknown, change unknown,* and *start unknown* and the relationship between the three.

In Grade 2, there is further evidence of exceptional instruction and practice involving place value. Students are required to indicate the place value of three-digit numbers, determine the value of each digit, make connections between representations of three-digit numbers, and connect number words and numbers written in base-ten numerals as sums of their base-ten units, as well as to say the number aloud. *GO Math!* students successfully extend their understanding of place value to hundreds, which lays the foundation for base-ten structural work in later grades. Assignments help students understand that a hundred is a unit of 100 ones, and that both tens and hundreds can be composed or decomposed. Using mental math, *GO Math!* students develop the academic language required to use place value and properties of operations to explain why addition and subtraction strategies work.

GO Math! materials offer hands-on instruction and practice with measuring tools so that students understand that *one* represents a length beginning at the zero mark on a ruler and ending at 1, not the number 1 itself. The inverse relationship between the size of a unit of length and the number of units required to measure a length are well illustrated and explained.

GO Math! Grades 3–5

The GIMET-QR algebra-progression statements in the 3–5 elementary grade span are drawn from the Operations and Algebraic Thinking, Number and Operations in Base Ten, Number and Operations—Fractions, and Measurement and Data domains.

In the intermediate grades in GO Math!, the instruction, including the explanations and connections that foster the deep development of the concepts and skills that are part of the algebra progression in these grades, the Math Talk prompts that promote engagement and interaction between students and teacher as well as among students, and the assignments that cement the learning all fully support the algebra-progression statements in the GIMET-QR.

Grade 3

Grade 3 students in GO Math! have many meaningful opportunities to represent and solve contextual multiplication and division problems for unknown products, unknown group sizes, and unknown numbers of groups. Students illustrate equal groups and arrays/area representations, which lays the foundation for algebraic expressions. GO Math! emphasizes the academic language students need to explain their reasoning about unknown products, group sizes, and numbers of groups. Students understand that in equal groups, the roles of the factors differ. Assignments ensure that students are facile with columns and rows in arrays. Students manipulate rectangular arrays to visualize and more fully understand the Commutative Property of Multiplication. When solving for unknowns in problem situations, students make connections among problems, manipulate representations, and link equations to representations. Students build their algebraic perspective when making these connections. GO Math! assignments encourage students to model and apply the properties of multiplication and the relationship between multiplication and division by requiring them to illustrate the properties and relationship with drawings and equations; to make the connection that two factors are quotients of related division problems; and to relate the product, factors, or quotients to contextual problem situations.

GO Math! facilitates the development of fluency with multiplication and division by modeling decomposing and composing products that are known in order to find an unknown product. Assignments require students to explain the relationship between area and multiplication and addition, represent it in different ways, and then apply their understanding to problems involving multiplication and area.

GO Math! fully supports students' understanding of fractions as they move beyond the fraction language they learned in prior grades. Students partition a whole into equal parts and visualize unit fractions as the basic building blocks of fractions. Students use the number line to show that fractions are numbers and that unit fractions can be the measure of length. This extensive, hands-on work with fractions serves as a stepping stone from arithmetic to algebra and is consistent with the latest research on effective fraction instruction as outlined in the Institute of Education Sciences guide *Developing Effective Fractions Instruction for Kindergarten through 8th Grade* (Siegler et al., 2010) and NCTM's *Developing Essential Understanding of Rational Numbers for Teaching Mathematics in Grades 3–5* (Barnett-Clarke et al., 2010).

GO Math! materials help students conceptualize area as the amount of two-dimensional space in a bounded region and to measure it by choosing a unit of area. Students explain how they connect area to multiplication and addition. Assignments require students to determine the areas of rectilinear figures by composing and decomposing them into non-overlapping areas and adding the parts. This sophisticated way of finding area is applied to contextual problem situations.

Grade 4

In **Grade 4** multiplication and division, students focus on distinguishing multiplicative comparison from additive comparison. GO Math! instruction emphasizes that in an additive comparison, one asks what amount can be added to one quantity to result in the other; in multiplicative comparison, one asks what factor would multiply one quantity to result in another. The specificity and academic language for comparisons in GO Math! help prepare students for formal algebra and sophisticated courses in later years. Likewise, multistep contextual problems that require students to interpret remainders are assigned.

Just as in Grade 3, work with fractions is integral to building a solid foundation for formal algebra. In *GO Math!* Grade 4, students illustrate addition as putting together so that they understand the way fractions are built from unit fractions. Renaming a mixed number to a fraction is considered to be a case of fraction addition, whereas renaming an improper fraction as a mixed number is decomposition.

When comparing two decimals, *GO Math!* students use the meaning of decimals as fractions and make sure to compare fractions with the same denominator. This promotes a deeper understanding of rational numbers.

Grade 5

Grade 5 students in *GO Math!* explain how multiplying a number by a power of 10 "shifts" every digit to the left. They use place value to explain patterns in the number of zeroes in products of whole numbers, powers of 10 and exponents, and the location of the decimal point in products of decimals with powers of 10. Assignments require students to connect the academic language of multiples to powers in order to understand multiplication with exponentiation. Students explain patterns when multiplying whole numbers or decimals by powers of 10.

Work with fractions at this level involves multiplication and division. With *GO Math!* materials, students connect the interpretation of a fraction as division to an understanding of division as equal sharing. Students make the connection between fraction multiplication and finding the area of a rectangle.

With *GO Math!*, students interpret multiplication of fractions as scaling in several ways. Without multiplying, they compare the size of the product to the size of one factor on the basis of the size of the other factor. Students explain why multiplying a given number by a fraction greater than 1 results in a product greater than the given number. Likewise, they explain why multiplying a fraction by a fraction less than 1 results in a product less than the given number. *GO Math!* students view multiplication as an operation that "stretches or shrinks" by a scale factor, which leads them to reason multiplicatively with continuous quantities.

Grade 5 students find the volume of a solid figure composed of two non-overlapping right rectangular prisms by adding the volumes of the parts. In *GO Math!*, students use this method to complete a space architecture project and justify how their design meets the specific volume criterion.

GO Math! Grades 6–8

The GIMET-QR algebra-progression statements in the middle grades are drawn from the domains The Number System, Ratios and Proportional Relationships, and Expressions and Equations.

The *GO Math!* instructional models, materials, and assignments for this grade span make meaningful connections with the concepts and skills taught in prior years and fully prepare students for algebra courses and beyond in high school.

Grade 6

The **Grade 6** instruction and assignments in *GO Math!* provide many opportunities for students to use story contexts and visual models to develop and deepen their understanding of fraction division. These opportunities help connect the relation between multiplication and division to fraction division.

The number line is extended to include negative numbers so that students can investigate negative numbers in context when describing magnitude and direction. Students use the number line to compare numbers based on their relative positions rather than their magnitudes. To avoid confusion with distance from zero and absolute value, *GO Math!* provides students contextual problems where it makes sense to compare the relative positions of two rational numbers and to compare their absolute values, and to witness where these two comparisons run in different directions.

GO Math! instruction on the concepts of ratio and rate is focused on the proportional relationship between two quantities. *GO Math!* assignments require students to explain their solutions to ratio and rate-reasoning problems. To support their explanations, the materials provide instruction in the use of tables of equivalent ratios, tape diagrams (bar models), double-number line diagrams, and the unit rate *a/b* associated with a ratio *a:b*.

In Grade 6, students connect their previous understanding of arithmetic to algebraic expressions and equations. With *GO Math!*, students use mathematical terms to explain how one or more parts of an expression correspond to the quantities in a contextual problem. Students interpret the structure of an expression in terms of a context. Work with numerical expressions prepares students for work with algebraic expressions. *GO Math!* supports this transition by instructing students to leave numerical expressions unevaluated, which prepares students for constructing the algebraic equation to solve the problem.

GO Math! assignments require students to use the process of reasoning to find the number which makes an equation true. This process includes checking whether a given number is a solution. Students work toward finding a standard method for solving equations, but they begin by studying examples and looking for structure. Their study leads to understanding that every occurrence of a given variable has the same value throughout the solution procedure.

Students then show their understanding of quantitative relationships between dependent and independent variables. They analyze the relationship between the variables by using graphs and tables, and they explain how these relate to the equation. This work with two variables prepares students for later work with functions.

Grade 7

The **Grade 7** *GO Math!* materials define a proportional relationship and then use that definition to determine if a relationship is proportional. Students examine situations carefully to determine the existence of a proportional relationship. *GO Math!* emphasizes the importance of structure and language by prompting students to look for and understand the roles of the terms *for every, for each,* and *per*. Teachers are reminded of typical misconceptions involving proportional relationships and offered suggestions for how to avoid them. The program explains the correspondences between representations including tables, equations, graphs, diagrams, and verbal descriptions. Students are required to test for equivalent ratios by using a table or by graphing on a coordinate plane and to show how the unit rate appears in each representation.

GO Math! students add and subtract rational numbers and represent the addition and subtraction on a horizontal or vertical number line. *GO Math!* materials demonstrate that each directed line segment has a direction, a beginning, and an end. When these directed line segments are linked, the second line segment begins at the end of the first one. Students realize that if the second line segment is going in the opposite direction to the first, then it can backtrack over the first and essentially cancel all or part of it out. This realization effectively lays the foundation for work with vectors in high school.

Students in *GO Math!* learn to simplify general linear expressions with rational coefficients. Students extend their prior understanding of order of operations and applied properties of operations to linear expressions that have more operations and whose transformations require an understanding of the rules for multiplying negative numbers. Here again, the *GO Math!* teacher notes identify typical student misconceptions in simplifying expressions and offer suggestions for addressing them.

Grade 8

In **Grade 8**, *GO Math!* students apply the properties of integer exponents to generate equivalent numerical expressions. Requiring the rule $10^a \cdot 10^b = 10^{a+b}$ to hold when a and b are integers leads to the definition of the meaning of powers with 0 and negative exponents. Students prepare for learning the properties of exponents in high school by working systematically with the square root and cube root symbols in *GO Math!* Assignments require students to express and perform calculations with very large or very small numbers by using scientific notation.

GO Math! materials illustrate the connections between proportional relationships, lines, and linear equations. Students start to build a unified notion of the concept of function, leading them to compare two different proportional relationships represented in different ways. Students understand that the connection between the unit rate in a proportional relationship and the slope of its graph depends on a connection with the geometry of similar triangles.

Students use a function to model a linear relationship between two quantities. They determine the rate of change, which is the slope of the line that is the graph of the function. Students read, compute, or approximate the rate of change from a table or graph. To foster understanding of relationships between quantities, *GO Math!* assignments ask students to describe the relationships quantitatively and to pay attention to the general shape of the graph without concern for the numerical values.

The *GO Math!* K–8 program presents a coherent algebra learning progression as illustrated by its content alignment to the GIMET-QR. Its comprehensive representation of the algebra progressions in its materials and assignments, combined with an instructional design that engages learners in developing not only procedural fluency, but deep conceptual understanding, is clear evidence that *GO Math!* is a high-quality mathematics program that fully prepares students for high school mathematics courses and beyond.

Bibliography

Barnett-Clarke, Carne, William Fisher, Rick Marks, and Sharon Ross. *Developing Essential Understanding of Rational Numbers for Teaching Mathematics in Grades 3–5*. Reston, VA: NCTM, 2010.

Council of the Great City Schools. Grade-Level Instructional Materials Evaluation Tool-Quality Review (GIMET-QR). Washington, DC: Council of the Great City Schools. http://www.cgcs.org/page/475

National Council of Teachers of Mathematics. *Principles and Standards for School Mathematics*. Edited by NCTM. Reston, VA: NCTM, 2000.

National Mathematics Advisory Panel. *Foundations for Success: The Final Report of the National Mathematics Advisory Panel*. Washington, DC: U.S. Department of Education, 2008.

"Progress to Algebra in Grades K–8." In "K–8 Publishers' Criteria for the Common Core State Standards for Mathematics," 8. 20 July 2012. http://www.corestandards.org/assets/Math_Publishers_Criteria_K-8_Summer%202012_FINAL.pdf

Siegler, Robert, Thomas Carpenter, Francis (Skip) Fennell, David Geary, James Lewis, Yukari Okamoto, Laurie Thompson, and Jonathan Wray, J. *Developing Effective Fractions Instruction for Kindergarten Through 8th Grade* (NCEE #2010-4039). Washington, DC: National Center for Education Evaluation and Regional Assistance, Institute of Education Sciences, U.S. Department of Education, 2010. Retrieved from whatworks.ed.gov/publications/practiceguides.

Progress to Algebra in Grades K–8

K	1	2	3	4
	Represent and solve problems involving addition and subtraction		Represent and solve problems involving multiplication and division	Use the four operations with whole numbers to solve problems
Know number names and the count sequence	Understand and apply properties of operations and the relationship between addition and subtraction	Represent and solve problems involving addition and subtraction	Understand properties of multiplication and the relationship between multiplication and division	Generalize place value understanding for multi-digit whole numbers
Count to tell the number of objects	Add and subtract within 20	Add and subtract within 20	Multiply and divide within 100	Use place value understanding and properties of operations to perform multi-digit arithmetic
Compare numbers	Work with addition and subtraction equations	Understand place value	Solve problems involving the four operations, and identify and explain patterns in arithmetic	
Understand addition as putting together and adding to, and understand subtraction as taking apart and taking from	Extend the counting sequence	Use place value understanding and properties of operations to add and subtract	Develop understanding of fractions as numbers	Extend understanding of fraction equivalence and ordering
Work with numbers 11–19 to gain foundations for place value	Understand place value	Measure and estimate lengths in standard units	Solve problems involving measurement and estimation of intervals of time, liquid volumes, and masses of objects	Build fractions from unit fractions by applying and extending previous understandings of operations
	Use place value understanding and properties of operations to add and subtract	Relate addition and subtraction to length		
			Geometric measurement: understand concepts of area and relate area to multiplication and to addition	Understand decimal notation for fractions, and compare decimal fractions
	Measure lengths indirectly and by iterating length units			

5	6	7	8
Understand the place value system	Apply and extend previous understandings of multiplication and division to divide fractions by fractions	Apply and extend previous understanding of operations with fractions to add, subtract, multiply, and divide rational numbers	Work with radical and integer exponents
Perform operations with multi-digit whole numbers and decimals to hundredths	Apply and extend previous understandings of numbers to the system of rational numbers		Understand the connections between proportional relationships, lines, and linear equations
Use equivalent fractions as a strategy to add and subtract fractions	Understand ratio concepts and use ratio reasoning to solve problems	Analyze proportional relationships and use them to solve real-world and mathematical problems	Analyze and solve linear equations and pairs of simultaneous linear equations
Apply and extend previous understandings of multiplication and division to multiply and divide fractions	Apply and extend previous understandings of arithmetic to algebraic expressions	Use properties of operations to generate equivalent expressions	Define, evaluate, and compare functions
Geometric measurement: understand concepts of volume and relate volume to multiplication and to addition	Reason about and solve one-variable equations and inequalities	Solve real-life and mathematical problems using numerical and algebraic expressions and equations	Use functions to model relationships between quantities
Graph points in the coordinate plane to solve real-world and mathematical problems*	Represent and analyze quantitative relationships between dependent and independent variables		

*Indicates a cluster that is well thought of as part of a student's progress to algebra, but that is currently not designated as Major by one or both of the assessment consortia in their draft materials. Apart from the asterisked exception, the clusters listed here are a subset of those designated as Major in both of the assessment consortia's draft documents.

Problem Types

Addition and Subtraction Problem Types

	Result Unknown	**Change Unknown**	**Start Unknown**
Add To	A glass contained $\frac{2}{3}$ cup of orange juice. Then $\frac{1}{4}$ cup of pineapple juice was added. How much juice is in the glass now? *Situation and Solution equation[1]:* $\frac{2}{3} + \frac{1}{4} = c$	A glass contained $\frac{2}{3}$ cup of orange juice. Then some pineapple juice was added. Now the glass contains $\frac{11}{12}$ cup of juice. How much pineapple juice was added? *Situation equation:* $\frac{2}{3} + p = \frac{11}{12}$ *Solution equation:* $p = \frac{11}{12} - \frac{2}{3}$	A glass contained some orange juice. Then $\frac{1}{4}$ cup of pineapple juice was added. Now the glass contains $\frac{11}{12}$ cup of juice. How much orange juice was in the glass to start? *Situation equation:* $r + \frac{1}{4} = \frac{11}{12}$ *Solution equation:* $r = \frac{11}{12} - \frac{1}{4}$
Take From	Micah had a ribbon $\frac{5}{6}$ yard long. He cut off a piece $\frac{1}{3}$ yard long. What is the length of the ribbon that is left? *Situation and Solution equation:* $\frac{5}{6} - \frac{1}{3} = s$	Micah had a ribbon $\frac{5}{6}$ yard long. He cut off a piece. Now the ribbon is $\frac{1}{2}$ yard long. What is the length of the ribbon he cut off? *Situation equation:* $\frac{5}{6} - c = \frac{1}{2}$ *Solution equation:* $c = \frac{5}{6} - \frac{1}{2}$	Micah had a ribbon. He cut off a piece $\frac{1}{3}$ yard long. Now the ribbon is $\frac{1}{2}$ yard long. What was the length of the ribbon he started with? *Situation equation:* $r - \frac{1}{3} = \frac{1}{2}$ *Solution equation:* $r = \frac{1}{2} + \frac{1}{3}$

	Total Unknown	**Addend Unknown**	**Both Addends Unknown**
Put Together/ Take Apart	A baker combines $\frac{3}{4}$ cup of white flour and $\frac{1}{2}$ cup of wheat flour. How much flour is this altogether? | $\frac{3}{4}$	$\frac{1}{2}$ | t *Situation and Solution equation:* $\frac{3}{4} + \frac{1}{2} = t$	Of the $1\frac{1}{4}$ cups of flour a baker uses, $\frac{3}{4}$ cup is white flour. The rest is wheat flour. How much wheat flour does the baker use? | $\frac{3}{4}$	w | $1\frac{1}{4}$ *Situation equation:* $1\frac{1}{4} = \frac{3}{4} + w$ *Solution equation:* $w = 1\frac{1}{4} - \frac{3}{4}$	A baker uses $1\frac{1}{4}$ cups of flour. Some is white flour and some is wheat flour. How much of each type of flour does the baker use? | f	w | $1\frac{1}{4}$ *Situation equation:* $1\frac{1}{4} = f + w$

[1]A situation equation represents the structure (action) in the problem situation. A solution equation shows the operation used to find the answer.

	Difference Unknown	**Larger Unknown**	**Smaller Unknown**
Compare[2]	At a zoo, the female rhino weighs $1\frac{3}{4}$ tons. The male rhino weighs $2\frac{1}{2}$ tons. How much **more** does the **male rhino** weigh than the female rhino?	***"MORE"* VERSION SUGGESTS OPERATION.** At a zoo, the female rhino weighs $1\frac{3}{4}$ tons. The **male rhino** weighs $\frac{3}{4}$ **ton more** than the female rhino. How much does the male rhino weigh?	***"FEWER / LESS"* VERSION SUGGESTS OPERATION.** At a zoo, the male rhino weighs $2\frac{1}{2}$ tons. The **female rhino** weighs $\frac{3}{4}$ **ton less** than the male rhino. How much does the female rhino weigh?
	At a zoo, the female rhino weighs $1\frac{3}{4}$ tons. The male rhino weighs $2\frac{1}{2}$ tons. How much **less** does the **female** rhino weigh than the male rhino?	***"FEWER / LESS"* VERSION SUGGESTS WRONG OPERATION.** At a zoo, the female rhino weighs $1\frac{3}{4}$ tons. The **female rhino** weighs $\frac{3}{4}$ **ton less** than the male rhino. How much does the male rhino weigh?	***"MORE"* VERSION SUGGESTS WRONG OPERATION.** At a zoo, the male rhino weighs $2\frac{1}{2}$ tons. The **male rhino** weighs $\frac{3}{4}$ **ton more** than the female rhino. How much does the female rhino weigh?

M | $2\frac{1}{2}$
F | $1\frac{3}{4}$ | d

Situation equation:
$1\frac{3}{4} + d = 2\frac{1}{2}$ or
$d = 2\frac{1}{2} - 1\frac{3}{4}$
Solution equation:
$d = 2\frac{1}{2} - 1\frac{3}{4}$

M | m
F | $1\frac{3}{4}$ | $\frac{3}{4}$

Situation and Solution equation:
$1\frac{3}{4} + \frac{4}{5} = m$

M | $2\frac{1}{2}$
F | f | $\frac{3}{4}$

Situation equation:
$f = 2\frac{1}{2} - \frac{3}{4}$ or
$f + \frac{3}{4} = 2\frac{1}{2}$
Solution equation:
$f = 2\frac{1}{2} - \frac{3}{4}$

[2]A comparison sentence can always be said in two ways. One way uses *more*, and the other uses *fewer* or *less*.

Multiplication and Division Problem Types

	Unknown Product	Group Size Unknown	Number of Groups Unknown
Equal Groups	Maddie ran around a $\frac{1}{4}$-mile track 16 times. How far did she run?	Maddie ran around a track 16 times. She ran 4 miles in all. What is the distance around the track?	Maddie ran around a $\frac{1}{4}$-mile track. She ran a total distance of 4 miles. How many times did she run around the track?
	Situation and Solution equation: $16 \times \frac{1}{4} = n$	*Situation equation:* $16 \times d = 4$ *Solution equation:* $d = 4 \div 16$	*Situation equation:* $t \times \frac{1}{4} = 4$ *Solution equation:* $t = 4 \div \frac{1}{4}$

	Unknown Product	Unknown Factor	Unknown Factor
Arrays	An auditorium has 58 rows with 32 seats in each row. How many seats are in the auditorium?	An auditorium has 58 rows with the same number of seats in each row. There are 1,856 seats in all. How many seats are in each row?	The 1,856 seats in an auditorium are arranged in rows of 32. How many rows of seats are there?
	Situation and Solution equation: $58 \times 32 = t$	*Situation equation:* $58 \times s = 1,856$ *Solution equation:* $s = 1,856 \div 58$	*Situation equation:* $r \times 32 = 1,856$ *Solution equation:* $r = 1,856 \div 32$
Area	A poster has a length of 1.2 meters and a width of 0.7 meter. What is the area of the poster? 1.2 0.7 [A]	A poster has an area of 0.84 square meter. The length of the poster is 1.2 meters. What is the width of the poster? 1.2 w [0.84]	A poster has an area of 0.84 square meter. The width of the poster is 0.7 meter. What is the length of the poster? l 0.7 [0.84]
	Situation and Solution equation: $1.2 \times 0.7 = A$	*Situation equation:* $1.2 \times w = 0.84$ *Solution equation:* $w = 0.84 \div 1.2$	*Situation equation:* $l \times 0.7 = 0.84$ *Solution equation:* $l = 0.84 \div 0.7$

Unknown Product	Unknown Factor	Unknown Factor

Compare

LARGER UNKNOWN

Sam has 5 times as many goldfish as Brady has. Brady has 3 goldfish. How many goldfish does Sam have?

		s		

Sam | 3 | | 3 | 3 | 3 |

Brady | 3 |

Situation and Solution equation:
$5 \times 3 = s$

SMALLER UNKNOWN

Sam has 5 times as many goldfish as Brady has. Sam has 15 goldfish. How many goldfish does Brady have?

15

Sam | b | b | b | b | b |

Brady | b |

Situation equation:
$5 \times b = 15$

Solution equation:
$b = 15 \div 5$

MULTIPLIER UNKNOWN

Sam has 15 goldfish. Brady has 3 goldfish. The number of goldfish Sam has is how many times the number Brady has?

15

Sam | |

Brady | 3 |

Situation equation:
$n \times 3 = 15$

Solution equation:
$n = 15 \div 3$

SMALLER UNKNOWN

Brady has $\frac{1}{5}$ times as many goldfish as Sam has. Sam has 15 goldfish. How many goldfish does Brady have?

15

Sam | b | b | b | b | b |

Brady | b |

$\frac{1}{5}$ of 15

Situation and Solution equation:
$\frac{1}{5} \times 15 = b$

LARGER UNKNOWN

Brady has $\frac{1}{5}$ times as many goldfish as Sam has. Brady has 3 goldfish. How many goldfish does Sam have?

s

Sam | | | | | |

Brady | 3 |

$\frac{1}{5}$ of s

Situation equation:
$\frac{1}{5} \times s = 3$

Solution equation:
$s = 3 \div \frac{1}{5}$

MULTIPLIER UNKNOWN

Sam has 15 goldfish. Brady has 3 goldfish. The number of goldfish Brady has is how many times the number Sam has?

15

Sam | |

Brady | 3 |

Situation equation:
$n \times 15 = 3$

Solution equation:
$n = 3 \div 15$

Fluency with Whole Numbers and Decimals

Project: In the Chef's Kitchen . . . . SE—2 . . . . . TE—2

STUDENT RESOURCES | TEACHER RESOURCES

1 Place Value, Multiplication, and Expressions . . . . SE—3 . . . . TE—3

Domains Operations and Algebraic Thinking
Number and Operations in Base Ten

○ 5.OA.A   Write and interpret numerical expressions.

■ 5.NBT.A   Understand the place value system.

■ 5.NBT.B   Perform operations with multi-digit whole numbers and with decimals to hundredths.

Common Core State Standards 5.OA.A.1, 5.OA.A.2, 5.NBT.A.1, 5.NBT.A.2, 5.NBT.B.5, 5.NBT.B.6

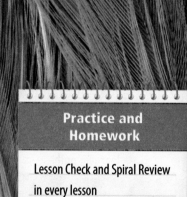

		STUDENT RESOURCES	TEACHER RESOURCES

Practice and Homework

Lesson Check and Spiral Review in every lesson

Common Core MATHEMATICAL PRACTICES

1. Make sense of problems and persevere in solving them.

2. Reason abstractly and quantitatively.

3. Construct viable arguments and critique the reasoning of others.

4. Model with mathematics.

5. Use appropriate tools strategically.

6. Attend to precision.

7. Look for and make use of structure.

8. Look for and express regularity in repeated reasoning.

Personal Math Trainer

Look for this symbol for a gateway to your personalized learning path!

STUDENT RESOURCES | TEACHER RESOURCES

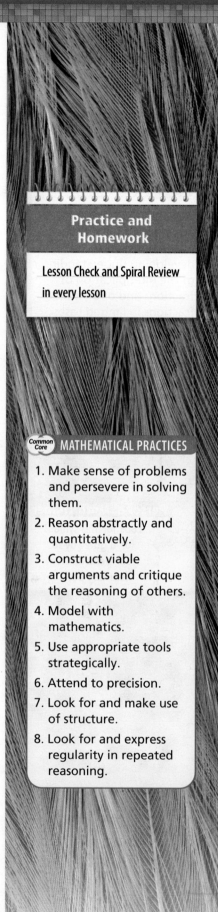

Practice and Homework

Lesson Check and Spiral Review in every lesson

MATHEMATICAL PRACTICES

1. Make sense of problems and persevere in solving them.
2. Reason abstractly and quantitatively.
3. Construct viable arguments and critique the reasoning of others.
4. Model with mathematics.
5. Use appropriate tools strategically.
6. Attend to precision.
7. Look for and make use of structure.
8. Look for and express regularity in repeated reasoning.

Key: SE—Student Edition; **TE**—Teacher Edition

Critical Area

Personal Math Trainer

Look for this symbol for a gateway to your personalized learning path!

Operations with Fractions

Real World Project: The Rhythm Track . . . . SE—348 . . TE—348

	STUDENT RESOURCES	TEACHER RESOURCES

6 Add and Subtract Fractions with Unlike Denominators . . . . SE—349 . . TE—349

Domains Operations and Algebraic Thinking
Number and Operations–Fractions

◯ 5.OA.A   Write and interpret numerical expressions.

▢ 5.NF.A   Use equivalent fractions as a strategy to add and subtract fractions.

Common Core State Standards 5.OA.A.2, 5.NF.A.1, 5.NF.A.2

STUDENT RESOURCES   TEACHER RESOURCES

Domain   Number and Operations–Fractions

◼   5.NF.B   Apply and extend previous understandings of multiplication and division to multiply and divide fractions.
Common Core State Standards   5.NF.B.4a, 5.NF.B.4b, 5.NF.B.5a, 5.NF.B.5b, 5.NF.B.6

> **Practice and Homework**
>
> Lesson Check and Spiral Review in every lesson

Common Core **MATHEMATICAL PRACTICES**

1. Make sense of problems and persevere in solving them.
2. Reason abstractly and quantitatively.
3. Construct viable arguments and critique the reasoning of others.
4. Model with mathematics.
5. Use appropriate tools strategically.
6. Attend to precision.
7. Look for and make use of structure.
8. Look for and express regularity in repeated reasoning.

STUDENT RESOURCES   TEACHER RESOURCES

Domain   Number and Operations–Fractions

◼   5.NF.B   Apply and extend previous understandings of multiplication and division to multiply and divide fractions.
Common Core State Standards   5.NF.B.3, 5.NF.B.7a, 5.NF.B.7b, 5.NF.B.7c

Key: SE—Student Edition; **TE**—Teacher Edition

© Houghton Mifflin Harcourt Publishing Company • Image Credits: (r) Photodisc/Getty Images

Critical Area

Common Core **CRITICAL AREA**

Developing understanding of volume.

Personal Math Trainer

Look for this symbol for a gateway to your personalized learning path!

Geometry and Measurement

Real World **Project: Space Architecture**.................. SE—**529** . . TE—**529**

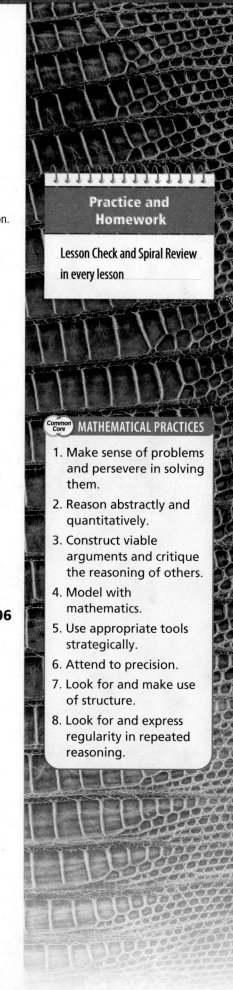

Practice and Homework

Lesson Check and Spiral Review in every lesson

Common Core MATHEMATICAL PRACTICES

1. Make sense of problems and persevere in solving them.
2. Reason abstractly and quantitatively.
3. Construct viable arguments and critique the reasoning of others.
4. Model with mathematics.
5. Use appropriate tools strategically.
6. Attend to precision.
7. Look for and make use of structure.
8. Look for and express regularity in repeated reasoning.

Key: SE—Student Edition; **TE**—Teacher Edition

© Houghton Mifflin Harcourt Publishing Company • Image Credits: (r) ©Corbis

End-of-Year Resources

Review Projects

Getting Ready for Grade 6

Key: P—Online Projects; **PG**—Planning Guide

Teacher Notes

Online Projects

Review Project:

The Forester

CRITICAL AREA Extending division to 2-digit divisors, integrating decimal fractions into the place value system and developing understanding of operations with decimals to hundredths, and developing fluency with whole number and decimal operations

Print Resources

• Planning Guide, p. PG42

Review Project:

Designing Backpacks

CRITICAL AREA Developing fluency with addition and subtraction of fractions, and developing understanding of the multiplication of fractions and of division of fractions in limited cases (unit fractions divided by whole numbers and whole numbers divided by unit fractions)

Print Resources

• Planning Guide, p. PG44

Review Project:

A Space Capsule

CRITICAL AREA Developing understanding of volume

Print Resources

• Planning Guide, p. PG46

 Animated Math Models

✓ **Assessment**

MM HMH Mega Math

iT iTools

P Projects

ABC Multimedia eGlossary

 Getting Ready Lessons build on Grade 5 content and prepare students for Grade 6 content.

Daily Pacing Chart

Review Projects	Lessons	Assessment	Total
3 days	20 days	2 days	25 days

LESSON 5

Relate Decimals and Percents

COMMON CORE   4.NF.C.6, 6.RP.A.3c

Resources

• Student Lesson Pages, Online
• Planning Guide, p. PG56

LESSON 10

Rates

COMMON CORE   4.NF.A.1, 6.RP.A.2

Resources

• Student Lesson Pages, Online
• Planning Guide, p. PG66

LESSON 15

Polygons on a Coordinate Grid

COMMON CORE   5.G.A.1, 6.G.A.3

Resources

• Student Lesson Pages, Online
• Planning Guide, p. PG78

LESSON 20

Analyze Histograms ✓

COMMON CORE   3.MD.B.3, 6.SP.B.4

Resources

• Student Lesson Pages, Online
• Planning Guide, p. PG88

LESSON 1

Compare Fractions and Decimals

COMMON CORE   5.NBT.A.3b, 6.NS.C.7b

Resources

• Student Lesson Pages, Online
• Planning Guide, p. PG48

LESSON 6

Fractions, Decimals, and Percents ✓

COMMON CORE   4.NF.C.6, 6.RP.A.3c

Resources

• Student Lesson Pages, Online
• Planning Guide, p. PG58

LESSON 11

Distance, Rate, and Time ✓

COMMON CORE   5.NBT.B.6, 6.RP.A.3b

Resources

• Student Lesson Pages, Online
• Planning Guide, p. PG68

LESSON 16

Area of a Parallelogram

COMMON CORE   4.MD.A.3, 6.G.A.1

Resources

• Student Lesson Pages, Online
• Planning Guide, p. PG80

LESSON 2 — **Order Fractions and Decimals**

COMMON CORE   5.NBT.A.3b, 6.NS.C.7b

Resources
- Student Lesson Pages, Online
- Planning Guide, p. PG50

LESSON 3 — **Factor Trees**

COMMON CORE   4.OA.B.4, 6.NS.B.4

Resources
- Student Lesson Pages, Online
- Planning Guide, p. PG52

LESSON 4 — **Model Percent**

COMMON CORE   4.NF.C.7, 6.RP.A.3c

Resources
- Student Lesson Pages, Online
- Planning Guide, p. PG54

LESSON 7 — **Divide Fractions by a Whole Number**

COMMON CORE   5.NF.B.7c, 6.NS.A.1

Resources
- Student Lesson Pages, Online
- Planning Guide, p. PG60

LESSON 8 — **Ratios**

COMMON CORE   3.NF.A.1, 6.RP.A.1

Resources
- Student Lesson Pages, Online
- Planning Guide, p. PG62

LESSON 9 — **Equivalent Ratios**

COMMON CORE   4.NF.A.1, 6.RP.A.3a

Resources
- Student Lesson Pages, Online
- Planning Guide, p. PG64

LESSON 12 — **Understand Integers**

COMMON CORE   5.G.A.1, 6.NS.C.5

Resources
- Student Lesson Pages, Online
- Planning Guide, p. PG72

LESSON 13 — **Algebra • Write and Evaluate Expressions**

COMMON CORE   5.OA.A.2, 6.EE.A.2c

Resources
- Student Lesson Pages, Online
- Planning Guide, p. PG74

LESSON 14 — **Algebra • Understand Inequalities**

COMMON CORE   5.NBT.A.3b, 6.EE.B.8

Resources
- Student Lesson Pages, Online
- Planning Guide, p. PG76

LESSON 17 — **Median and Mode**

COMMON CORE   5.MD.B.2, 6.SP.B.5c

Resources
- Student Lesson Pages, Online
- Planning Guide, p. PG82

LESSON 18 — **Finding the Average**

COMMON CORE   5.MD.B.2, 6.SP.B.5c

Resources
- Student Lesson Pages, Online
- Planning Guide, p. PG84

LESSON 19 — **Histograms**

COMMON CORE   3.MD.B.3, 6.SP.B.4

Resources
- Student Lesson Pages, Online
- Planning Guide, p. PG86

✓ Assessment

An Assessment Check Mark following a lesson title indicates that a Checkpoint or Getting Ready Test is available for assessment after completing the lesson.

Checkpoints and Getting Ready Tests can be found in the online Getting Ready Lessons and Resources.

Extending division to 2-digit divisors, integrating decimal fractions into the place value system and developing understanding of operations with decimals to hundredths, and developing fluency with whole number and decimal operations

1 INTRODUCE THE PROJECT

The Review Project for this critical area connects whole number operations and the use of data to the field of forestry management. Foresters use a variety of math skills to take measurements and make calculations that help them with the many decisions they make concerning the long-term health of forests.

▶ Overview: The Forester

A forester is responsible for managing forests for the present as well as for the future. Forest management plans need to keep in mind the needs of the timber industry as well as the needs of plants and animals that live in the forest environment. Foresters are responsible for deciding which trees to keep and which to harvest and how many seedlings to plant and where to plant them.

▶ Questions

Pose questions like the ones below to help students understand that they will use the mathematics they learn every day and in the future. Ask:

- **What does a forester do?** Possible answer: He or she checks on the health of trees, decides which trees to harvest, and plants seedlings.

- **What math skills does a forester use?** Possible answer: A forester uses measurement, addition, subtraction, multiplication, and division to help make decisions about the present and future health of forests.

Before students calculate the number of trucks needed to transport the logs, explain that a *board foot* is a unit of measure. One board foot is a 1-foot square of wood that is 1 inch thick. Ask:

- **Is a board foot a measure of length, area, or volume? Explain.** Volume; possible explanation: A board foot is a measure of volume because it has 3 dimensions.

Make sure students have the information and the understanding they need to complete the Review Project on their own or with a partner.

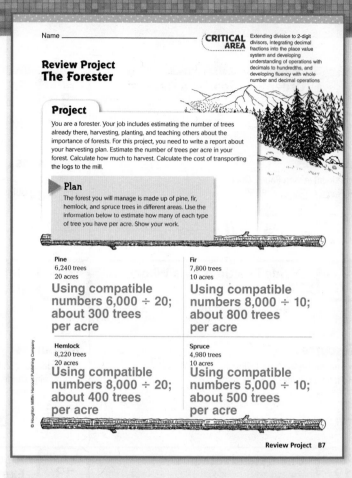

Name _____

CRITICAL AREA

Extending division to 2-digit divisors, integrating decimal fractions into the place value system and developing understanding of operations with decimals to hundredths, and developing fluency with whole number and decimal operations

Review Project
The Forester

Project

You are a forester. Your job includes estimating the number of trees already there, harvesting, planting, and teaching others about the importance of forests. For this project, you need to write a report about your harvesting plan. Estimate the number of trees per acre in your forest. Calculate how much to harvest. Calculate the cost of transporting the logs to the mill.

▶ **Plan**

The forest you will manage is made up of pine, fir, hemlock, and spruce trees in different areas. Use the information below to estimate how many of each type of tree you have per acre. Show your work.

Pine
6,240 trees
20 acres
Using compatible numbers 6,000 ÷ 20; about 300 trees per acre

Fir
7,800 trees
10 acres
Using compatible numbers 8,000 ÷ 10; about 800 trees per acre

Hemlock
8,220 trees
20 acres
Using compatible numbers 8,000 ÷ 20; about 400 trees per acre

Spruce
4,980 trees
10 acres
Using compatible numbers 5,000 ÷ 10; about 500 trees per acre

Review Project B7

▶ **Put It Together**

Throughout the year, you will harvest and transport some of the trees in your forest. The trees you harvest vary in height but will all be cut into 8-foot logs. Use the information below to show the total number of logs you will get from the trees you cut.

Harvest

Tree Height (ft)	Number of Trees	Number of Logs
64	6	$6 \times (64 \div 8) = 48$
112	1	$112 \div 8 = 14$
48	15	$15 \times (48 \div 8) = 90$
96	4	$4 \times (96 \div 8) = 48$
80	10	$10 \times (80 \div 8) = 100$
Total number of logs:		**300**

Amazing Fact:
Every year in the United States, each person on average uses the equivalent of one tree that is 100 feet tall and 16 inches in diameter to fulfill their wood and paper needs.

Amazing Fact:
It would take about 10,000 board feet of wood to make an 1,800 square foot home.

Transport

- Each log yields about 80 board feet of wood.
- Each truck holds 4,000 board feet of wood.

Your timber is harvested and now it must be trucked to the mills. How many log trucks will you need to carry 300 logs? Explain.

Possible answer: 4,000 ÷ 80 = 50 logs per truck; 300 ÷ 50 = 6 trucks needed to carry 300 logs.

B8

Name _____

Reflect

A forest fire has burned 10 acres of your forest. You order 3,000 seedlings to replant the forest. You must choose some of each type of tree. Show your order below and explain why you made the choices you did.

Reforestation   Possible answers shown.

Tree Species	Containers of 250 Seedlings	Total Seedlings	Seedlings per acre
Black Spruce Medium growth, partial sun, moist soil.	1	250	$250 \div 10 = 25$
Ponderosa Pine Medium to fast growth, full sun, well drained soil.	3	750	$750 \div 10 = 75$
Douglas Fir Slow growth, full sun, tolerates a variety of soils.	5	1,250	$1,250 \div 10 = 125$
Hemlock Fast growth, full sun, well drained soil.	3	750	$750 \div 10 = 75$
Total:	12 containers	3,000 seedlings	300 seedlings per acre

Possible Answer: I would order more Douglas Firs because they like sun and can grow in a variety of soils. After a forest fire there will be very little shade. I chose fewer Black Spruces because they need some shade to grow.

© Houghton Mifflin Harcourt Publishing Company

Review Project **B9**

Go Beyond

One of your goals as a forester is to help school children learn more about forestry and the steps they can take to keep the world green. At a recent school visit, students in one class tell you that they are going to sell tree-shaped cookies to raise money to buy seedlings. Their goal is to earn enough money to buy a seedling for each student in the school. They will make their community a greener place by planting their trees around their school and at a local park. Help the students figure out the details for their fund raiser.

Amazing Fact: Each year, timber companies plant more than 5 new trees for every man, woman, and child in the United States. That's a lot of trees!

- There are 400 students in the school.
- There are 16 students in this class.
- 5 Seedlings cost $1
- Cookies will sell for $0.25 each.

1. How much money do they need to earn?
   $400 \div 5 = \$80$

2. How many cookies do they need to sell to earn enough money?
   4 cookies cost $1
   $80 \times 4 = 320$ cookies

3. If each student in the class makes the same number of cookies, how many cookies will each student make?
   $320 \div 16 = 20$ cookies

4. How can you check to make sure you answers are correct? **Explain.**
   I can multiply the number of cookies each student makes, 20, by the cost per cookie, $0.25, to find the amount each student will make. I can multiply that amount by the number of students in the class, which should give me the amount the class needs to earn to buy the seedlings. $20 \times \$0.25 = \$5.00$; $\$5.00 \times 16 = \$80.00$. So, my answer checks.

B10

© Houghton Mifflin Harcourt Publishing Company

Online Projects, pp. B9–B10

---

② DO THE PROJECT

▶ The Forester

- Before students begin work, have them read the opening sentences of the Project and preview the remaining sections. Ask students to explain in their own words what they need to do. Discuss strategies for rounding numbers to estimate an answer. Review different methods for dividing multi-digit numbers.

③ EXTEND THE PROJECT

Have students do research to learn more about forestry and the uses of the wood we get from trees. Pose the following questions to get them started.

- **What are the measurements of a *cord* of wood?** A cord is a stack of logs 4 feet high, 4 feet deep, and 8 feet long.

- **About how many of each of these things could be produced from 1 cord of wood?**
  Possible estimated amounts are given.

8 ½ in. × 11 in. sheets of paper	about 90,000
rocking chairs	about 30
postage stamps	about 4.5 million
toothpicks	about 7.5 million

 Portfolio You may suggest that students place completed Review Projects in their portfolios.

 Performance Assessment

Project Scoring Rubric

3   Demonstrates full understanding of the project. Uses the important facts to produce a complete response with no errors. Presents the project clearly and completely.

2   Demonstrates a thorough understanding of the project. Uses the important facts to produce a complete response that may contain one or two errors. Presents the project clearly, without noticing errors.

1   Demonstrates a partial understanding of the project. Uses the important facts but makes errors in applying them. Makes a good, but incomplete, attempt at presenting the project.

0   Demonstrates little understanding of the project. Fails to use the important facts and to present accurate and complete conclusions.

Developing fluency with addition and subtraction of fractions, and developing understanding of the multiplication of fractions and of division of fractions in limited cases (unit fractions divided by whole numbers and whole numbers divided by unit fractions)

1 INTRODUCE THE PROJECT

The Review Project for this critical area connects operations with fractions to the design of backpacks. Designers of backpacks, duffel bags, and other kinds of gear for carrying things use a variety of math skills as they make patterns and prototypes for their designs.

▶ Overview: Designing Backpacks

Geometry and measurement are key elements in creating a successful backpack design. Not only must a backpack be comfortable and functional, but it must also be attractive. Attention to measuring the component parts is crucial to ensure that the backpack will have the correct volume and be comfortable for the consumer to use.

▶ Questions

Pose questions like the ones below to help students understand that they will use the mathematics they learn every day and in the future. Ask:

- **Why is the size of a backpack important?** Possible answer: A backpack that is the wrong size may not have enough room for everything that needs to be carried or it may not fit the person using it.

- **What does a backpack designer do?** Possible answer: A backpack designer makes patterns for prototype models of backpacks that are both functional and comfortable for consumers.

- **What math skills does a backpack designer use?** Possible answer: Careful measuring of each part of the pattern is important so that when the backpack is made, it will match its design and the pieces will fit together correctly. Fractions and decimals may be used for measuring. Decimals are also used to figure out the cost of the materials needed for the design.

Make sure students have the information and understanding they need to complete the Review Project on their own or with a partner.

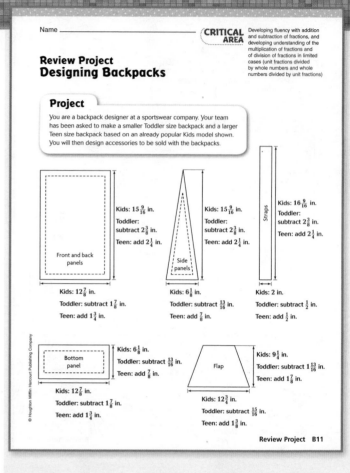

Name _____

CRITICAL AREA Developing fluency with addition and subtraction of fractions, and developing understanding of the multiplication of fractions and of division of fractions in limited cases (unit fractions divided by whole numbers and whole numbers divided by unit fractions)

**Review Project
Designing Backpacks**

Project

You are a backpack designer at a sportswear company. Your team has been asked to make a smaller Toddler size backpack and a larger Teen size backpack based on an already popular Kids model shown. You will then design accessories to be sold with the backpacks.

Front and back panels
Kids: $15\frac{9}{16}$ in.
Toddler: subtract $2\frac{3}{8}$ in.
Teen: add $2\frac{1}{4}$ in.

Side panels
Kids: $15\frac{9}{16}$ in.
Toddler: subtract $2\frac{3}{8}$ in.
Teen: add $2\frac{1}{4}$ in.

Straps
Kids: $16\frac{9}{16}$ in.
Toddler: subtract $2\frac{3}{8}$ in.
Teen: add $2\frac{1}{4}$ in.

Kids: $12\frac{7}{8}$ in.
Toddler: subtract $1\frac{7}{8}$ in.
Teen: add $1\frac{3}{4}$ in.

Kids: $6\frac{1}{8}$ in.
Toddler: subtract $\frac{13}{16}$ in.
Teen: add $\frac{7}{8}$ in.

Kids: 2 in.
Toddler: subtract $\frac{1}{2}$ in.
Teen: add $\frac{1}{2}$ in.

Bottom panel
Kids: $6\frac{1}{8}$ in.
Toddler: subtract $\frac{13}{16}$ in.
Teen: add $\frac{7}{8}$ in.

Flap
Kids: $9\frac{1}{4}$ in.
Toddler: subtract $1\frac{13}{16}$ in.
Teen: add $1\frac{7}{8}$ in.

Kids: $12\frac{7}{8}$ in.
Toddler: subtract $1\frac{7}{8}$ in.
Teen: add $1\frac{3}{4}$ in.

Kids: $12\frac{3}{4}$ in.
Toddler: subtract $1\frac{15}{16}$ in.
Teen: add $1\frac{1}{8}$ in.

© Houghton Mifflin Harcourt Publishing Company

Review Project B11

▶ Plan

Complete the chart. Find the height and width for each panel of the toddler and teen backpacks, using the information on page B11.

	Backpack Dimensions (in inches)					
	Toddler		Kids		Teen	
Panels	Height	Width	Height	Width	Height	Width
Front and back	$13\frac{3}{16}$	11	$15\frac{9}{16}$	$12\frac{7}{8}$	$17\frac{13}{16}$	$14\frac{5}{8}$
Side	$13\frac{3}{16}$	$5\frac{5}{16}$	$15\frac{9}{16}$	$6\frac{1}{8}$	$17\frac{13}{16}$	7
Bottom	$5\frac{5}{16}$	11	$6\frac{1}{8}$	$12\frac{7}{8}$	7	$14\frac{5}{8}$
Flap	$7\frac{7}{16}$	$11\frac{13}{16}$	$9\frac{1}{4}$	$12\frac{3}{4}$	$11\frac{1}{8}$	$14\frac{1}{8}$
Straps	$14\frac{3}{16}$	$1\frac{1}{2}$	$16\frac{9}{16}$	2	$18\frac{13}{16}$	$2\frac{1}{2}$

▶ Put It Together

Use rulers, construction paper, and tape to make models of the three backpack sizes. How do you know which sides to tape together?

Possible answer: The panel names and the measurements help me know which panels go together.

© Houghton Mifflin Harcourt Publishing Company

B12

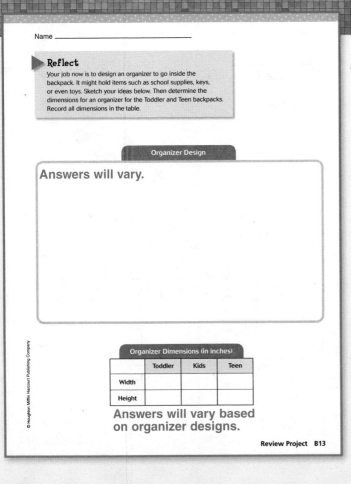

Name _____

Reflect
Your job now is to design an organizer to go inside the backpack. It might hold items such as school supplies, keys, or even toys. Sketch your ideas below. Then determine the dimensions for an organizer for the Toddler and Teen backpacks. Record all dimensions in the table.

Organizer Design

Answers will vary.

Organizer Dimensions (in inches)

	Toddler	Kids	Teen
Width			
Height			

Answers will vary based on organizer designs.

Review Project   B13

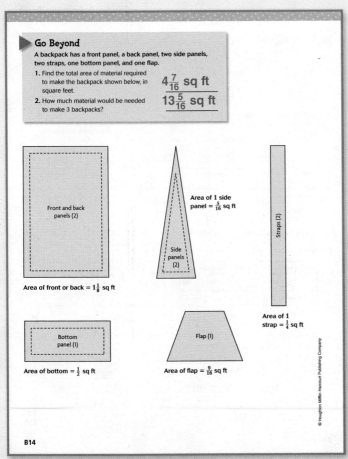

Go Beyond
A backpack has a front panel, a back panel, two side panels, two straps, one bottom panel, and one flap.

1. Find the total area of material required to make the backpack shown below, in square feet. $4\frac{7}{16}$ sq ft

2. How much material would be needed to make 3 backpacks? $13\frac{5}{16}$ sq ft

Front and back panels (2)

Area of front or back = $1\frac{1}{8}$ sq ft

Side panels (2)

Area of 1 side panel = $\frac{5}{16}$ sq ft

Straps (2)

Area of 1 strap = $\frac{1}{4}$ sq ft

Bottom panel (1)

Area of bottom = $\frac{1}{2}$ sq ft

Flap (1)

Area of flap = $\frac{9}{16}$ sq ft

B14

2 DO THE PROJECT

▶ Designing Backpacks

- Before students begin work, have them read the opening sentences of the Project and preview the remaining sections. Ask students to explain in their own words what they need to do.

- Discuss strategies that students have learned for adding and subtracting like and unlike fractions.

- To help students get started, display three backpacks of different designs. Label the backpacks with sticky notes marked A, B, and C. Ask for volunteers to measure the height, width, and depth of each backpack to the nearest quarter inch. Write the measurements on the board.

  How much wider is Backpack A than Backpack B?

  How much taller is Backpack A than Backpack C?

3 EXTEND THE PROJECT

Have two or more students work together to measure parts of a backpack and record its dimensions.

Ask students to add $2\frac{1}{2}$ in. to each of their measurements to reflect the size of a larger version of that backpack. Then have them subtract $2\frac{1}{2}$ in. from each of the original measurements to reflect the size of a smaller version.

Portfolio   You may suggest that students place completed Review Projects in their portfolios.

Performance Assessment

Project Scoring Rubric

3   Demonstrates full understanding of the project. Uses the important facts to produce a complete response with no errors. Presents the project clearly and completely.

2   Demonstrates a thorough understanding of the project. Uses the important facts to produce a complete response that may contain one or two errors. Presents the project clearly, without noticing errors.

1   Demonstrates a partial understanding of the project. Uses the important facts but makes errors in applying them. Makes a good, but incomplete, attempt at presenting the project.

0   Demonstrates little understanding of the project. Fails to use the important facts and to present accurate and complete conclusions.

Developing understanding of volume

1 INTRODUCE THE PROJECT

The Review Project for this critical area connects geometry and measurement to designing the interior spaces in a space capsule. Aerospace engineers use a variety of math skills to design storage areas and other equipment that are necessary for space exploration.

▶ Overview: A Space Capsule

A space capsule must be designed carefully in order to meet the astronauts' basic needs in a comfortable working environment while at the same time conforming to strict aeronautical standards. Aerospace and industrial engineers must work closely to find the right balance between safety, comfort, practicality, and function.

▶ Questions

Pose questions like the ones below to help students understand that they will use the mathematics they learn every day and in the future. Ask:

- **What special skills and knowledge might be needed to design a space capsule?** Possible answers: Knowing what kinds of materials are needed so that the space vehicle can withstand the trip through space and safely return to Earth, and determining what the astronauts need to be safe and comfortable during their journey.

- **What do aerospace engineers do?** Possible answer: They design vehicles for space exploration and work with other engineers to find the right shape, size, materials, and design for space capsules.

- **What math skills do aerospace and industrial engineers use?** Possible answer: They use many areas of math including measurement, geometry, algebra, fractions, decimals, multiplication, division, addition, and subtraction.

Make sure students have the information and understanding they need to complete the Review Project on their own or with a partner.

Name _____

CRITICAL AREA Developing understanding of volume

**Review Project
A Space Capsule**

Project

You are an aerospace engineer. One of your responsibilities is to make the best use of space on the capsule. The astronauts must be able to move about comfortably and have plenty of room for food, water, and supplies.

For this project, you must decide how you can store the greatest number of battery packs in containers in the storage area of a space capsule.

Plan

The storage area on the space capsule has 2,000 cubic inches of space to store the battery packs. The battery packs will be packed in one type of container, and then as many of these containers as possible will be placed in the available space in the storage area.

Find the volume of each container.

Rectangular Prism	Length (in.)	Width (in.)	Height (in.)	Volume (cu in.)
Container 1	10	10	3	300
Container 2	5	5	10	250
Container 3	10	10	10	1,000

Review Project **B15**

Put It Together

The storage area available is shaped like a rectangular prism, shown below. Find the width of the storage space.

length = 20 in.
height = 10 in.   Volume = 2,000 cu in.
width = **10** in.

Each battery pack is a cube with edges that are 2 inches. Use the dimensions of each container to determine which holds the most battery packs.

Think: Do the battery packs completely fill the length, width, or height of the container?

Approximate Measurement of Containers (in Battery Packs)			
	Length	Width	Height	Volume
Container 1	5	5	1	25
Container 2	2	2	5	20
Container 3	5	5	5	125

Container **3** holds the most battery packs.

Estimate the volume of the storage area in containers. Then use the volume of each container in battery packs to decide which container should be used.

Approximate Storage Area Measurement (in Containers)					Total Number of Battery Packs that Fit in the Storage Area
	Length	Width	Height	Volume	
Container 1	2	1	3	6	150
Container 2	4	2	1	8	160
Container 3	2	1	1	2	250

Which container should you use? **Explain** how you decided.

Container 3. Possible explanation: The volume of each battery pack is 8 cu in. The most battery packs held in 2,000 cu in. is 2,000 ÷ 8, or 250 battery packs. So, Container 3 holds the greatest possible number of battery packs.

B16

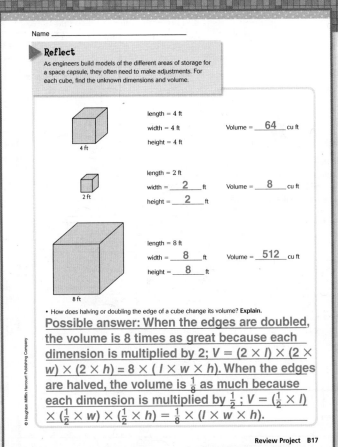

Name _____

▶ **Reflect**

As engineers build models of the different areas of storage for a space capsule, they often need to make adjustments. For each cube, find the unknown dimensions and volume.

length = 4 ft
width = 4 ft   Volume = __64__ cu ft
height = 4 ft
4 ft

length = 2 ft
width = __2__ ft   Volume = __8__ cu ft
height = __2__ ft
2 ft

length = 8 ft
width = __8__ ft   Volume = __512__ cu ft
height = __8__ ft
8 ft

• How does halving or doubling the edge of a cube change its volume? **Explain.**

<u>Possible answer: When the edges are doubled,</u>
<u>the volume is 8 times as great because each</u>
<u>dimension is multiplied by 2; $V = (2 \times l) \times (2 \times$</u>
<u>$w) \times (2 \times h) = 8 \times (l \times w \times h)$. When the edges</u>
<u>are halved, the volume is $\frac{1}{8}$ as much because</u>
<u>each dimension is multiplied by $\frac{1}{2}$; $V = (\frac{1}{2} \times l)$</u>
<u>$\times (\frac{1}{2} \times w) \times (\frac{1}{2} \times h) = \frac{1}{8} \times (l \times w \times h)$.</u>

Review Project **B17**

▶ **Go Beyond**

You have been asked to help design other interior spaces in a space capsule that will store the astronauts' personal items. Complete the chart below to show your suggestions.

Personal Item	Dimensions (in inches)	Storage Shape with Dimensions (sketch)	Volume
	8 wide 15 deep 16 high	**Answers will vary.**	
	16 wide 16 deep 18 high		
	15 wide 10 deep 2 high		

B18

2 DO THE PROJECT

▶ A Space Capsule

- Before students begin work, have them read the opening sentences of the Project and preview the remaining sections. Ask students to explain in their own words what they need to do.

- Review the terms *cube*, *rectangular prism*, and *volume*. Draw a cube on the board. Label one edge "3 ft." Ask students to explain how to find the volume of the cube.

- Have students look around the room for examples of rectangular prisms. Ask them to estimate the length, width, and height of each prism, and then to use their estimates to estimate the volume of each.

3 EXTEND THE PROJECT

Have students build 3-dimensional shapes and put them together to form a storage area for their own "space capsules." Ask them to describe their completed work to the class in terms of both the 2- and 3-dimensional shapes that they used. Provide students with construction materials, such as recycled boxes, containers, clay, toothpicks, and straws to make these models.

You may suggest that students place completed Review Projects in their portfolios.

Project Scoring Rubric

3 Demonstrates full understanding of the project. Uses the important facts to produce a complete response with no errors. Presents the project clearly and completely.

2 Demonstrates a thorough understanding of the project. Uses the important facts to produce a complete response that may contain one or two errors. Presents the project clearly, without noticing errors.

1 Demonstrates a partial understanding of the project. Uses the important facts but makes errors in applying them. Makes a good, but incomplete, attempt at presenting the project.

0 Demonstrates little understanding of the project. Fails to use the important facts and to present accurate and complete conclusions.

LESSON 1

Compare Fractions and Decimals

LESSON AT A GLANCE

Common Core Standards
Understand the place value system.
5.NBT.A.3b Read, write, and compare decimals to thousandths. Compare two decimals to thousandths based on meanings of the digits in each place, using >, =, and < symbols to record the results of comparisons.

Apply and extend previous understandings of numbers to the system of rational numbers.

6.NS.C.7b Understand ordering and absolute value of rational numbers. Write, interpret, and explain statements of order for rational numbers in real-world contexts.

Lesson Objective
Compare decimals, fractions, and mixed numbers on a number line.

Materials
MathBoard, Number Lines (see *eTeacher Resources*)

☑ Animated Math Models
*i*T *i*Tools: Fractions
〰 HMH Mega Math

---

1 TEACH and TALK GO DIGITAL • Animated Math Models

▶ **Unlock the Problem**

Core MATHEMATICAL PRACTICES

Help students understand how they can use a number line to compare fractions, decimals, and mixed numbers.

Distribute number lines to students. Discuss the meaning of the word *benchmark*: for fractions and decimals on a number line, they are marks between whole numbers that are a useful point of reference. Help students to identify some fractional benchmarks, such as $\frac{1}{4}, \frac{1}{2}, \frac{3}{4}$, as well as decimal benchmarks, such as 0.25, 0.50, and 0.75.

• **Find 4.7, $4\frac{3}{5}$, and 4.35 on the number line. How can you tell which one has the greatest value?** The number that is farthest to the right on the number line is the greatest.

Try This!

• **Mark $\frac{1}{5}$ and 0.2 on the number line. What do you see?** They are equal to each other.

• **How does $\frac{5}{8}$ compare to 0.75?** $\frac{5}{8}$ is less than 0.75.

PG48   Planning Guide

This lesson builds on decimal and fraction concepts presented in Chapters 3–8 and prepares students for comparisons between decimals and fractions taught in Grade 6.

Name _____

Compare Fractions and Decimals

Essential Question How can you compare decimals, fractions, and mixed numbers on a number line?

 Unlock the Problem Real World

The Tech Club compared the weights of three cell phones. Estéban's phone weighed 4.7 ounces. Jill's phone weighed $4\frac{3}{5}$ ounces. Mona's phone weighed 4.35 ounces. Who has the phone with the lightest weight?

You can use a number line to compare fractions and decimals.

Remember: Greater values on a number line lie farther to the right.

🔑 **Compare the values on a number line.**

STEP 1 Locate some benchmarks.
• Benchmark decimals: 4, 4.25, 4.5, 4.75, 5...
• Benchmark mixed numbers: 4, $4\frac{1}{4}$, $4\frac{1}{2}$, $4\frac{3}{4}$, 5...

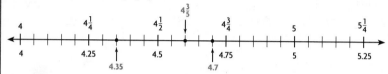

STEP 2 Mark the weight of each cell phone on the number line.
• Find the location of 4.7, $4\frac{3}{5}$, and 4.35.

Since $4.35 < 4\frac{3}{5} < 4.7$, Mona's phone is lightest.

• How can you identify the number with the least value?

Possible answer: The number that is farthest left on the number line has the least value.

Try This! Compare $\frac{1}{5}$, $\frac{5}{8}$, and 0.2. Which number has the greatest value?
• Mark each value on a number line.

Possible explanation: They are at the same place on the number line.

The greatest number is ___$\frac{5}{8}$___. **Explain** how you decided.

Of the three numbers, $\frac{5}{8}$ is farthest to the right.

Math Talk Mathematical Practices
Explain how you can tell that $\frac{1}{5}$ and 0.2 are equal.

© Houghton Mifflin Harcourt Publishing Company

Getting Ready for Grade 6   **GR1**

GR: Practice, p. GRP1

Name _____   Lesson 1
Compare Fractions and Decimals

Locate each number on a number line.
Then complete the sentence.   **Check students' number lines.**
1. 0.6, $\frac{4}{5}$, 0.35

The number with the greatest value is ___$\frac{4}{5}$___

2. $3\frac{1}{2}$, 3.45, $3\frac{1}{4}$
The number with the greatest value is ___3.45___

3. $2\frac{1}{2}$, 2.65, $2\frac{3}{4}$
The number with the least value is ___2.65___

4. $4\frac{1}{2}$, $4\frac{1}{6}$, 4.85
The number with the greatest value is ___4.85___

5. 3.45, $3\frac{2}{5}$, $3\frac{1}{2}$
The number with the least value is ___$3\frac{2}{5}$___

Problem Solving Real World

6. Leonardo correctly answered 0.8 of the questions on his math exam. Liam correctly answered $\frac{4}{5}$ of the questions. Keira correctly answered $\frac{7}{10}$ of the questions. Who correctly answered the greatest number of questions?

___Liam___

7. Lana bought 1.25 pounds of ground beef at the market. Jada bought $1\frac{1}{2}$ pounds of ground beef. Willow bought 1.8 pounds of ground beef. Which person bought the least amount of ground beef?

___Lana___

GRP1

GR: Reteach, p. GRR1

Name _____   Lesson 1 Reteach
Compare Fractions and Decimals

Three friends compare the thicknesses of their textbooks. Julio's science book is 1.35 inches thick. Hannah's math book is $1\frac{1}{2}$ inches thick. Gabriela's history book is 1.9 inches thick. Who has the textbook with the least thickness?

You can use a number line to compare fractions and decimals.

Remember: On a number line, the number farthest to the left from 0 has the least value.

Step 1 Draw a number line. Locate some benchmarks on the number line.
Benchmark decimals: 1, 1.25, 1.5, 1.75, 2, …
Benchmark mixed numbers: 1, $1\frac{1}{4}$, $1\frac{1}{2}$, $1\frac{3}{4}$, 2, …

Step 2 Mark the thickness of each textbook on the number line.
Find the locations of 1.35, $1\frac{1}{2}$, and 1.9.

Since $1.35 < 1\frac{1}{2} < 1.9$, Julio's textbook has the least thickness.

For 1–2, identify the points on the number line. Then write the greater number.

1. point A as a fraction $1\frac{2}{5}$

2. point B as a decimal 1.15
$1\frac{2}{5}$ is greater than ___1.15___

Locate each number on a number line. Then complete the sentence.

3. $1\frac{3}{8}$, 1.85, 1.1 **Check students' number lines.**
The number with the greatest value is ___1.85___

Reteach   GRR1   Grade 6

---

*GR – Getting Ready Lessons and Resources (*www.thinkcentral.com*)

Share and Show

For 1–2, identify the points on the number line.
Then write the greater number.

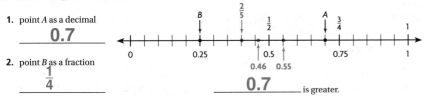

1. point *A* as a decimal
   0.7

2. point *B* as a fraction
   $\dfrac{1}{4}$

0.7 is greater.

Locate each number on a number line.
Then complete the sentence.

3. $0.55, \frac{2}{5}, 0.46$ **Check students' number lines.**

The number with the greatest value is **0.55**.

On Your Own

Locate each number on a number line. Then complete the sentence.

4. $0.4, \frac{3}{4}, 0.15$ **Check students' number lines.**

The number with the greatest value is $\dfrac{3}{4}$.

5. $2\frac{2}{3}, 2.45, 2\frac{2}{5}$

The number with the least value is $2\dfrac{2}{5}$.

6. $3.95, 3\frac{5}{6}, 3\frac{4}{5}$

The number with the greatest value is **3.95**.

Problem Solving

7. Hannah made 0.7 of her free throws in a basketball game. Abra made $\frac{9}{10}$ of her free throws. Dena made $\frac{3}{4}$ of her free throws. Who was the best shooter? **Explain.**

Abra; Possible explanation: On a number line, $\frac{9}{10}$ is farther right than the other two numbers, so Abra made more of her free throws than the other players.

GR2

© Houghton Mifflin Harcourt Publishing Company

2 PRACTICE

▶ **Share and Show • Guided Practice**
Encourage students to discuss how they chose the benchmark numbers for their number lines.

▶ **On Your Own • Independent Practice**
Some students may need one-on-one assistance as they identify the benchmarks. Encourage students to express relationships using symbols, such as <, >, or =.

▶ **Problem Solving** MATHEMATICAL PRACTICES
Remind students how to begin by showing relevant benchmark fractions on a number line.

3 SUMMARIZE

MATHEMATICAL PRACTICES

Essential Question

How can you compare decimals, fractions, and mixed numbers on a number line? Possible answer: Identify the benchmarks on the number line as decimals and fractions. Locate the value of each number on the number line and graph a point. The point that is farthest to the right on the number line represents the greatest number.

Math Journal WRITE Math
Explain how you can compare 0.65 and $\frac{3}{5}$.

LESSON 2

Order Fractions and Decimals

LESSON AT A GLANCE

Common Core Standards
Understand the place value system.
5.NBT.A.3b Read, write, and compare decimals to thousandths. Compare two decimals to thousandths based on meanings of the digits in each place, using >, =, and < symbols to record the results of comparisons.

Apply and extend previous understandings of numbers to the system of rational numbers.

6.NS.C.7b Understand ordering and absolute value of rational numbers. Write, interpret, and explain statements of order for rational numbers in real-world contexts.

Lesson Objective
Order decimals, fractions, and mixed numbers on a number line.

Materials
MathBoard, Number Lines (see *eTeacher Resources*)

 GO DIGITAL

☑ Animated Math Models
iT *i*Tools: Fractions
MMM HMH Mega Math

1 TEACH and TALK GO DIGITAL • Animated Math Models

▶ Unlock the Problem

Common Core MATHEMATICAL PRACTICES

Help students understand how to order decimals, fractions, and mixed numbers on a number line.

Distribute number lines to students. Review from the previous lesson the meaning of the term *benchmark*. Remind students that they can use benchmarks to compare quantities.

Read the problem aloud and help students to identify the decimal and fractional benchmarks. Have students work in pairs to locate each number on the number line.

- **Which number is greatest?** 0.97 **How can you tell?** It is farthest to the right on the number line.

- **Where is the number that has the least value?** It is farthest to the left.

Try This!

- **How do you know that 6.2 is greater than 6.03?** Possible answer: 6.2 is farther right on the number line than 6.03.

PG50   Planning Guide

This lesson builds on decimal and fraction concepts presented in Chapters 3–8 and prepares students for comparisons between decimals and fractions taught in Grade 6.

Name _____

Order Fractions and Decimals

Essential Question How can you order decimals, fractions, and mixed numbers on a number line?

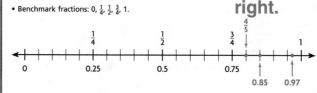 **Unlock the Problem** Real World

In tennis, Jocelyn's serve takes 0.97 of a second to reach her opponent. Dave's serve takes $\frac{4}{5}$ of a second. Monica's serve takes 0.85 of a second. Order the three serves from shortest to longest time.

🔒 Order the fractions and decimals on the number line.

STEP 1 Locate the benchmarks on the number line.
- Benchmark decimals: 0, 0.25, 0.5, 0.75, 1.
- Benchmark fractions: 0, $\frac{1}{4}$, $\frac{1}{2}$, $\frac{3}{4}$, 1.

- You want to order the times from shortest to longest. Should you read the numbers on the number line left to right or right to left?

Possible answer: Read left to right because the values increase from left to right.

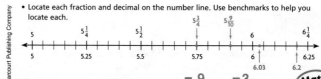

STEP 2 Locate 0.97, $\frac{4}{5}$, and 0.85 on the number line.

STEP 3 Order the fractions and decimals.

Remember: The point farthest to the left is the least value.

So, the times in order from shortest to longest are: $\frac{4}{5}$, 0.85 , 0.97 .

Try This! Order 6.03, $5\frac{9}{10}$, $5\frac{3}{4}$, and 6.2 from greatest to least.

- Locate each fraction and decimal on the number line. Use benchmarks to help you locate each.

From the greatest to least: 6.2 , 6.03 , $5\frac{9}{10}$, $5\frac{3}{4}$

Numbers to the right are greater than numbers to the left. So, I order the numbers from right to left.

Math Talk **Mathematical Practices**
How does the number line help you order numbers from greatest to least?

Getting Ready for Grade 6   GR3

© Houghton Mifflin Harcourt Publishing Company

GR: Practice, p. GRP2

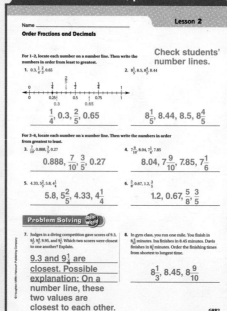

GR: Reteach, p. GRR2

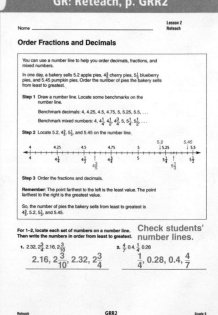

*GR – Getting Ready Lessons and Resources (*www.thinkcentral.com*)

Share and Show

Locate each number on the number line.
Then write the numbers in order from least to greatest.

1. $\frac{3}{5}$, 0.54, 0.35

   0.35, 0.54, $\frac{3}{5}$

For 2-3, locate each set of numbers on a number line.
Then write the numbers in order from greatest to least.

2. 1.16, $1\frac{1}{4}$, 1.37, $1\frac{1}{10}$

   1.37, $1\frac{1}{4}$, 1.16, $1\frac{1}{10}$

3. $\frac{5}{8}$, 0.5, $\frac{2}{5}$, 0.78

   Check students' number lines.

   0.78, $\frac{5}{8}$, 0.5, $\frac{2}{5}$

On Your Own

For 4-5, locate each number on a number line.
Then write the numbers in order from least to greatest.

4. 0.6, $\frac{1}{2}$, $\frac{2}{3}$, 0.39

   0.39, $\frac{1}{2}$, 0.6, $\frac{2}{3}$

5. $7\frac{1}{4}$, 7.4, $7\frac{3}{4}$, 7.77

   Check students' number lines.

   $7\frac{1}{4}$, 7.4, $7\frac{3}{4}$, 7.77

For 6-7, locate each number on a number line.
Then write the numbers in order from greatest to least.

6. $\frac{3}{10}$, 0.222, $\frac{3}{5}$, 0.53

   $\frac{3}{5}$, 0.53, $\frac{3}{10}$, 0.222

7. 2.96, $3\frac{1}{5}$, 3.48, $3\frac{1}{4}$

   Check students' number lines.

   3.48, $3\frac{1}{4}$, $3\frac{1}{5}$, 2.96

Problem Solving Real World

8. Judges in a skateboarding competition gave scores of 8.2, $8\frac{1}{3}$, $8\frac{4}{5}$, 8.44, and $8\frac{1}{5}$. Which two scores were closest to one another? **Explain**.

   8.2 and $8\frac{1}{5}$ are equal, so they are closest. Possible explanation: I saw on the number line that the two values were in the same place, so they were closest.

GR4

---

2 PRACTICE

▶ **Share and Show** • **Guided Practice**

Remind students to use fraction benchmarks when locating fractions and decimal benchmarks when locating decimals.

▶ **On Your Own** • **Independent Practice**

Students may need additional help identifying the benchmarks for each number line.

▶ **Problem Solving** Common Core MATHEMATICAL PRACTICES

Help students draw a number line that begins at 8 and ends at 9. Have students work together to identify useful fraction and decimal benchmarks between 8 and 9.

3 SUMMARIZE

Common Core MATHEMATICAL PRACTICES

Essential Question

How can you order decimals, fractions, and mixed numbers on a number line? Possible answer: First, put benchmarks on the number line. Then locate the numbers on the number line. You can read the numbers from least to greatest if you read the numbers on the line from left to right.

Math Journal WRITE ▸ Math

Draw a number line that begins at 4 and ends at 5. Mark and identify a mixed number and a decimal number on the number line. Then explain how you can tell which number is the greater of the two.

LESSON 3

Factor Trees

This lesson builds on finding factors presented in Grade 4, and prepares students for finding greatest common factors taught in Grade 6.

LESSON AT A GLANCE

Common Core Standards
Gain familiarity with factors and multiples.
4.OA.B.4 Find all factor pairs for a whole number in the range 1–100. Recognize that a whole number is a multiple of each of its factors. Determine whether a given whole number in the range 1–100 is a multiple of a given one-digit number. Determine whether a given whole number in the range 1–100 is prime or composite.

Compute fluently with multi-digit numbers and find common factors and multiples.
6.NS.B.4 Find the greatest common factor of two whole numbers less than or equal to 100 and the least common multiple of two whole numbers less than or equal to 12. Use the distributive property to express a sum of two whole numbers 1–100 with a common factor as a multiple of a sum of two whole numbers with no common factor.

Lesson Objective
Factor numbers using a factor tree.

Vocabulary
factor tree

Materials
MathBoard

1 TEACH and TALK

▶ **Unlock the Problem**

MATHEMATICAL PRACTICES

Have students read the problem. Emphasize that when writing a number as a product of prime number factors, each factor must be greater than 1 and can have only 1 and itself as factors. Draw the beginning of the factor tree, shown in Step 1, on the board.

- **What are some pairs of factors for 24?** 4×6, 3×8, 12×2

- **Write 24 at the top of your factor tree. Let's use 4 and 6 as the factors of 24. Do each of these factors have only 1 and itself as factors?** no

- **What are the factors of 4?** 2×2 **What are the factors of 6?** 2×3

- **Do each of the factors 2 and 3 have only 1 and itself as factors?** yes

Try This!

Have students use one of the other pairs of factors for 24 to complete the problem. Have students share their factor trees with the class.

Use Math Talk to check students' understanding of factored numbers and common factors.

PG52   Planning Guide

Name _____

Factor Trees

Essential Question How can you factor numbers using a factor tree?

🔑 **Unlock the Problem** Real World

Mr. Shu gives this puzzle to his math students.

"Write 24 as a product of factors that are prime. Remember that a prime number must be greater than 1 and can have only 1 and itself as factors."

You can use a diagram called a **factor tree** to find the factors of a number.

- Give an example of a number greater than 1 that has only 1 and itself as factors.

Possible answers:
2, 3, 5

🔑 Use a factor tree to find the prime number factors that have a product of 24.

STEP 1	**STEP 2**	**STEP 3**	**STEP 4**
Write the number to be factored at the top of the factor tree.	Write it as a product of any two factors. Think: $4 \times 6 = 24$	Write each factor as the product of two factors. Think: $2 \times 2 = 4$ and $2 \times 3 = 6$	Continue until each factor is a prime number. Think: $2 \times 1 = 2$ and $3 \times 1 = 3$ Write the factors that are prime numbers from least to greatest.
24	24 $\underline{4} \times \underline{6}$	24 4×6 $\underline{2} \times \underline{2} \times \underline{2} \times \underline{3}$	$\underline{2} \times \underline{2} \times \underline{2} \times \underline{3}$

So, $24 = \underline{2 \times 2 \times 2 \times 3}$.

Try This! Make a different factor tree for 24.

Check students' factor trees. Possible answer is given.

- Is the product of factors the same as in the Example? **Explain.**

Yes, the prime number factors are the same, no matter which factors I start with.

24
3×8
4×2
2×2

Math Talk **Mathematical Practices**

Explain how you can use factored numbers to find common factors.

See Planning Guide.

Getting Ready for Grade 6   GR5

GR: Practice, p. GRP3

Name _____   Lesson 3
Factor Trees

Use a factor tree to find prime factors.

Check students' factor trees.

1. 100
4×25
$2 \times 2 \times 5 \times 5$

2. 42
$2 \times 3 \times 7$

3. 54
$2 \times 3 \times 3 \times 3$

4. 56
$2 \times 2 \times 2 \times 7$

5. 60
$\times 2 \times 3 \times 5$

6. 90
$2 \times 3 \times 3 \times 5$

7. 120
$2 \times 2 \times 2 \times 3 \times 5$

8. 175
$5 \times 5 \times 5$

9. 300
$2 \times 2 \times 3 \times 5 \times 5$

Problem Solving Real World

10. What is the least number that has 4 odd factors that are all the same? Each factor is greater than 1, and can have only 1 and itself as factors.
Explain how you found the number.
81; Possible explanation: 3 is the least odd number greater than 1. Since the only factors of 3 are 1 and itself, find $3 \times 3 \times 3 \times 3$.

GRP3

GR: Reteach, p. GRR3

Name _____   Lesson 3
Reteach
Factor Trees

You can use a **factor tree** to show the factors of a number that are all prime numbers. Remember a prime number must be greater than 1, and have only 1 and itself as factors.

Use a factor tree to find the prime number factors that have a product of 18.

Step 1 Draw two branches below 18.

Step 2 Choose any two factors of 18. Try 6×3. Write the factors under the branches. Include the multiplication sign.

Step 3 Check if 6 and 3 are prime numbers. Think: $6 = 2 \times 3$ and $3 = 3 \times 1$. Draw branches below 6 and write the factors. Since 3 has only 1 and itself as factors, do not draw any branches below 3.

Step 4 Check if 2 and 3 are prime numbers. Think: $2 = 2 \times 1$ and $3 = 3 \times 1$. Each factor has only 1 and itself as a factor. Do not draw any more branches.

Write the factors from least to greatest. Use each factor that has only 1 and itself as a factor.

So, $18 = 2 \times 3 \times 3$.

18
6×3
2×3

Use a factor tree to find the prime number factors.

Check students' factor trees.

1. 12
$2 \times 2 \times 3$

2. 30
$2 \times 3 \times 5$

3. 50
$2 \times 5 \times 5$

Reteach
© Houghton Mifflin Harcourt Publishing Company   GRR3   Grade 5

---

*GR – Getting Ready Lessons and Resources (www.thinkcentral.com)

Share and Show

1. Use a factor tree to find the prime number factors that have a product of 210.

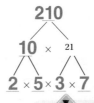

210

- Write 210 as a product of any two factors.

$$\underline{210} = \underline{10} \times 21$$

- Write each factor as the product of factors.

$$10 = \underline{2} \times \underline{5} \qquad 21 = \underline{3} \times \underline{7}$$

Now each factor has only $\underline{1}$ and itself as factors.

So, $210 = \underline{2} \times \underline{3} \times \underline{5} \times \underline{7}$.

! ERROR Alert
Remember to continue to factor a number if it has factors other than 1 and itself.

Use a factor tree to find the prime number factors.

Check students' factor trees.

2. 8

$$2 \times 2 \times 2$$

3. 45

$$3 \times 3 \times 5$$

4. 350

$$2 \times 5 \times 5 \times 7$$

On Your Own

Use a factor tree to find the prime number factors.

Check students' factor trees.

5. 36

$$2 \times 2 \times 3 \times 3$$

6. 72

$$2 \times 2 \times 2 \times 3 \times 3$$

7. 540

$$2 \times 2 \times 3 \times 3 \times 3 \times 5$$

Problem Solving (Real World)

Mr. Shu gave these problems to his math students. Solve.

8. Write 500 as a product of prime number factors. Each factor must be greater than 1 and can have only 1 and itself as factors.

$$2 \times 2 \times 5 \times 5 \times 5$$

9. Find a number that has four identical even factors. Each factor must be greater than 1 and can have only 1 and itself as factors.

$$2 \times 2 \times 2 \times 2 = 16$$

GR6

Use Math Talk to check students' understanding of factored numbers and common factors. Possible explanation: You can see what factors are the same for the two numbers; these would be common factors.

2 PRACTICE

▶ **Share and Show • Guided Practice**

Work through Exercise 1 with students. For Exercises 2–4, have students share the first two factors they chose for each factor tree. Remind students to write the prime number factors from least to greatest.

▶ **On Your Own • Independent Practice**

For Exercises 5–7, have students check their answers by multiplying the factors.

▶ **Problem Solving** (Common Core) **MATHEMATICAL PRACTICES**

For Exercise 8, have students tell the first two factors they chose for 500. For Exercise 9, make sure students understand that the only even number that has 1 and itself as its only factors is 2.

3 SUMMARIZE

(Common Core) **MATHEMATICAL PRACTICES**

Essential Question

How can you factor numbers using a factor tree? Possible answer: I can make a factor tree, choose a pair of factors of the number, continue factoring each factor until each resulting factor on the tree is greater than 1 and has only 1 and itself as factors.

Math Journal  Math

Draw two different factor trees for 40. Then write the factors for each factor tree from least to greatest.

LESSON 4

Model Percent

LESSON AT A GLANCE

Common Core Standards

Understand decimal notation for fractions, and compare decimal fractions.

4.NF.C.7 Compare two decimals to hundredths by reasoning about their size. Recognize that comparisons are valid only when the two decimals refer to the same whole. Record the results of comparisons with the symbols >, =, or <, and justify the conclusions, e.g., by using a visual model.

Understand ratio concepts and use ratio reasoning to solve problems.

6.RP.A.3c Use ratio and rate reasoning to solve real-world and mathematical problems, e.g., by reasoning about tables of equivalent ratios, tape diagrams, double number line diagrams, or equations. Find a percent of a quantity as a rate per 100 (e.g., 30% of a quantity means 30/100 times the quantity); solve problems involving finding the whole, given a part and the percent.

Lesson Objective

Express real world quantities as percents and use them to solve problems.

Materials

MathBoard, 10 × 10 grids (see *eTeacher Resources*)

1 TEACH and TALK

▶ Unlock the Problem

Common Core MATHEMATICAL PRACTICES

Write the word *percent* on the board. Tell students that percent means "per hundred" or "out of 100." Tell students that percents are similar to ratios and fractions. For example, sixty percent is the same as the fraction $\frac{60}{100}$ and the ratio 60 to 100.

▶ Example 1

Distribute the 10 × 10 grids. Verify with students that there are 10 rows of 10 squares, for a total of 100 squares. Direct students to shade 53 squares.

- **How many rows or columns did you shade?** 5 **How many extra squares?** 3 **How many out of 100 are shaded?** 53

- **How can you write this quantity as a fraction?** $\frac{53}{100}$ **as a percent?** 53%

▶ Example 2

- **What percent is represented by none of the squares being shaded?** 0% **half of the squares being shaded?** 50% **all of the squares being shaded?** 100%

PG54 Planning Guide

This lesson builds on decimals to hundredths presented in Grade 4, and prepares students for finding a percent of a quantity taught in Grade 6.

Name _____

Model Percent

Essential Question How can you express real world quantities as percents and use them to solve problems?

 Unlock the Problem Real World

Percent means "per hundred" or "out of 100." So, when you find percent you are finding a part of 100. Sixty percent, for example, means 60 out of 100. You can write percents using the percent symbol, %. So, 60 percent is written as 60%.

- What number is always compared in a percent?

  100

🔑 **Example 1** Name the percent that is shaded.

- 5 columns: 5 × 10 = 50.
- 3 squares: 3 × 1 = 3
- Total: 50 + 3 = 53 out of 100, or 53 percent is shaded.

🔑 **Example 2** Name the percent that is not shaded.

- 4 columns: 4 × 10 = 40.
- 7 squares: 7 × 1 = 7
- Total: 40 + 7 = 47 out of 100, or 47 percent is not shaded.

Try This! Use the number line. Tell what these percents mean: 0 percent, 50 percent, 100 percent.

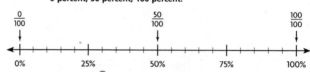

A. 0 percent means **0** out of 100, or none of the total.

B. 50 percent means **50** out of 100, or half of the total.

C. 100 percent means **100** out of 100, or all of the total.

50%; Possible explanation: On a number line 33% is closer to 50% than 0%.

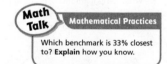 **Math Talk** **Mathematical Practices**

Which benchmark is 33% closest to? **Explain** how you know.

Getting Ready for Grade 6 **GR7**

GR: Practice, p. GRP4

Name _____ Lesson 4

Model Percent

Use the diagram to write the percent.

1. dark shading   2. light shading   3. not shaded

   10%   14%   76%

4. not shaded   5. dark shading   6. light shading

   30%   20%   50%

Write the closest benchmark for the percent.

7. 8%   8. 52%   9. 99 percent

   0%   50%   100%

10. 87%   11. 12 percent   12. 45%

   100%   0%   50%

Problem Solving Real World

13. Out of all the students who auditioned for a play, 43% received a role. About what percent of students who auditioned received roles? Explain.

50%. Possible explanation: 43% is closest to 50%.

14. The school cafeteria is holding an election for students to vote on which items they would like to see on the lunch menu. The choices for entrees are grilled chicken and veggie pizza. 36% of students vote for veggie pizza. Which item will be on the lunch menu?

Grilled chicken. Possible explanation: 36% is less than half, so more than half of the students must have voted for grilled chicken.

GRP4

GR: Reteach, p. GRR4

Name _____ Lesson 4
Reteach

Model Percent

Percent means "per hundred" or "out of 100." For example, 40 percent means 40 out of 100. You can write 40 percent as 40%.

You can use a decimal model like the one below to represent percents. The model has 100 squares. Each small square represents 1%. All 100 squares represent 100%.

Use the model to write the percent.

How many whole rows and single squares are shaded?

rows: **4**   single squares: **3**

What is shaded?

4 rows: 4 × 10 = **40**   single squares: 3 × 1 = **3**

Total: 40 + 3 = 43 out of 100 squares, or **43%** is shaded.

Shade the grid to show the percent.   Possible shadings are shown.

1. 16 percent   2. 83%

3. 45%   4. 97 percent

Reteach
GRR4   Grade 5

***GR** – Getting Ready Lessons and Resources (www.thinkcentral.com)

Share and Show

Use the diagram to write the percent.

1. How many whole columns and single squares are shaded?

7 columns, 4 single squares

2. What percent is shaded?

74%

3. What percent is unshaded?

26%

Shade the grid to show the percent.   **Possible shading shown.**

4. 20 percent

5. 86 percent

On Your Own

Use the diagram to write the percent.

6. light shading
30%

7. dark shading
52%

8. not shaded
18%

9. not shaded
44%

10. dark shading
20%

11. light shading
36%

Write the closest benchmark for the percent.

12. 48%
50%

13. 94%
100%

14. 4%
0%

Problem Solving

15. In an election between Warren and Jorge, Warren declared victory because he received 58 percent of the vote. Is he correct? **Explain.**

Yes; Possible explanation: He is correct because 58% is greater than half, or 50% of the vote.

GR8

2 PRACTICE

▶ **Share and Show •** Guided Practice

For Exercises 2 and 3, clarify with students that the percent shaded and the percent unshaded combined should add up to all of the grid, or 100%.

▶ **On Your Own •** Independent Practice

For Exercises 6–11, help students to check their work by adding up the three percents to see if the total is 100%.

▶ **Problem Solving**

Have students shade 58% of a grid and compare to half, or 50%, of the grid.

3 SUMMARIZE

 MATHEMATICAL PRACTICES

Essential Question

How can you express real world quantities as percents and use them to solve problems?

Possible answer: You can relate a real world quantity as a percent using a 10 × 10 grid and then compare its size to a benchmark: 0%, 50%, or 100%.

Math Journal WRITE ▸Math

A portion of a grid is shaded. Explain why the sum of the shaded and unshaded portions of the grid equals 100 percent of the grid.

LESSON 5

Relate Decimals and Percents

LESSON AT A GLANCE

Common Core Standards
Understand decimal notation for fractions, and compare decimal fractions.
4.NF.C.6 Use decimal notation for fractions with denominators 10 or 100.

Understand ratio concepts and use ratio reasoning to solve problems.
6.RP.A.3c Use ratio and rate reasoning to solve real-world and mathematical problems, e.g., by reasoning about tables of equivalent ratios, tape diagrams, double number line diagrams, or equations. Find a percent of a quantity as a rate per 100 (e.g., 30% of a quantity means 30/100 times the quantity); solve problems involving finding the whole, given a part and the percent.

Lesson Objective
Express decimals as percents and percents as decimals.

Materials
MathBoard, 10 × 10 grids (see *eTeacher Resources*)

GO DIGITAL   Animated Math Models

---

1 TEACH and TALK GO DIGITAL • Animated Math Models

▶ Unlock the Problem

MATHEMATICAL PRACTICES

Help students understand how to express decimals as percents and percents as decimals. Tell students that decimals and percents are two ways to express the same number. Distribute 10 × 10 grids to demonstrate an example.

Direct students to shade in 5 rows and 4 single squares on the grid. Clarify that they have shaded in 54 out of 100 squares. Tell students that they can express this as 54%, $\frac{54}{100}$, or 0.54.

- **Look at Example 1. How do you express this number as a fraction?** $\frac{42}{100}$ **as a percent?** 42% **as a decimal?** 0.42

- **Look at Example 2. How do you express this number as a fraction?** $\frac{19}{100}$ **as a percent?** 19% **as a decimal?** 0.19

- **How can you describe the pattern you see?**
  Possible description: The decimal has the same digits as the numerator of the fraction. The decimal point comes before the two digits. The percent has the same digits as the numerator with a % after them.

PG56 Planning Guide

This lesson builds on writing decimal notation for fractions presented in Grade 4, and prepares students for finding a percent of a quantity taught in Grade 6.

Name _____

Relate Decimals and Percents

Essential Question How can you express decimals as percents and percents as decimals?

🔑 Unlock the Problem Real World

Decimals and percents are two ways of expressing the same number. You can write a percent as a decimal. You can also write a decimal as a percent.

- In percent, the "whole" is 100. What is the "whole" in decimal form? **1.0, or 1.00**

Example 1 Model 0.42. Write 0.42 as a percent.

STEP 1 Write the decimal as a ratio.
0.42 = 42 hundredths = 42 out of 100.

STEP 2 Make a model that shows 42 out of 100.

STEP 3 Use the model to write a percent.
42 shaded squares = **42** percent, or **42**%

Example 2 Model 19 percent. Write 19% as a decimal.

STEP 1 Write the percent as a fraction.
19% = $\frac{19}{100}$

STEP 2 Make a model that shows 19 out of 100.

STEP 3 Use the model to write a decimal.
19 shaded squares out of 100 squares = **0.19**

Possible answer: The sale prices are half of the original prices.

Math Talk **Mathematical Practices**
Suppose a store is having a 50% off sale. What does this mean?

© Houghton Mifflin Harcourt Publishing Company

Getting Ready for Grade 6   GR9

GR: Practice, p. GRP5

Name _____   Lesson 5
Relate Decimals and Percents

Write the decimals as percents.
1. 0.30 **30%**   2. 0.48 **48%**   3. 0.25 **25%**   4. 0.87 **87%**
5. 0.09 **9%**   6. 0.5 **50%**   7. 0.02 **2%**   8. 0.1 **10%**
9. 0.37 **37%**   10. 0.3 **30%**   11. 0.89 **89%**   12. 0.09 **9%**

Write the percents as decimals.
13. 18 percent **0.18**   14. 47% **0.47**   15. 98 percent **0.98**   16. 12 percent **0.12**
17. 6 percent **0.06**   18. 21 percent **0.21**   19. 80 percent **0.80, or 0.8**   20. 7% **0.07**
21. 14 percent **0.14**   22. 52 percent **0.52**   23. 60 percent **0.60, or 0.6**   24. 1% **0.01**

Problem Solving Real World
25. In baseball, Anthony hit 0.63 of the pitches thrown at him. What percent of the pitches did Anthony miss? **37%**
26. In a theater, 0.85 of the seats are filled. What percent of the seats are empty? **15%**

GRP5

GR: Reteach, p. GRR5

Name _____   Lesson 5 Reteach
Relate Decimals and Percents

Decimals and percents are two ways of expressing a number. You can express a decimal as a percent and a percent as a decimal.

Model 0.26. Write 0.26 as a percent.
Step 1 Write the decimal as a ratio.
0.26 = 26 hundredths = 26 out of 100.
Step 2 Make a model that shows 26 out of 100.
Remember: 1 square represents 1 hundredth, or 1%.
Step 3 Use the model to write a percent.
26 shaded squares = **26** percent, or **26%**.
0.26 = 26%

Model 13 percent. Write 13% as a decimal.
Step 1 Write the percent as a fraction.
13% = $\frac{13}{100}$
Step 2 Make a model that shows 13 out of 100.
Step 3 Use the model to write a decimal.
13 shaded squares out of 100 squares = **0.13**
13% = 0.13

Use the model. Complete each statement.
1a. 0.89 = **89** out of 100
1b. How many squares are shaded? **89**
1c. What percent is shaded? **89%**

Write the percents as decimals.
2. 67% **0.67**   3. 14% **0.14**

Reteach
© Houghton Mifflin Harcourt Publishing Company
GRR5   Grade 5

---

*GR – Getting Ready Lessons and Resources (www.thinkcentral.com)

Share and Show

Use the model. Complete each statement.

1a. 0.68 = **68** out of 100

1b. How many squares are shaded?

68

1c. What percent is shaded?

68%

Write the percents as decimals.

2. 47 percent
0.47

3. 11 percent
0.11

 On Your Own

Write the decimals as percents.

4. 0.20
20%

5. 0.39
39%

6. 0.44
44%

7. 0.93
93%

8. 0.07
7%

9. 0.7
70%

10. 0.06
6%

11. 0.6
60%

Write the percents as decimals.

12. 12 percent
0.12

13. 31%
0.31

14. 99 percent
0.99

15. 13 percent
0.13

16. 4 percent
0.04

17. 14 percent
0.14

18. 90 percent
0.90, or 0.9

19. 9%
0.09

Problem Solving Real World

20. In basketball, Linda made 0.56 of her shots. What percent of her shots did Linda miss?

44 percent

GR10

© Houghton Mifflin Harcourt Publishing Company

 PRACTICE

▶ **Share and Show** • **Guided Practice**

Encourage students to note the similarities and the differences between the equivalent decimals and percents. Point out the location of the decimal point in each number.

▶ **On Your Own** • **Independent Practice**

Students may need to be reminded to not include the decimal point when writing each number as a percent.

▶ **Problem Solving** **MATHEMATICAL PRACTICES**

Encourage students to use 10 × 10 grids to make a model of the information to help them solve the problem.

③ SUMMARIZE

MATHEMATICAL PRACTICES

Essential Question

How can you express decimals as percents and percents as decimals? Possible answer: I can write the decimal as a fraction with 100 as the denominator, make a model that shows the number out of 100, and use the model to write a percent. I can write a percent as a fraction with 100 as the denominator and then write the fraction as a decimal.

Math Journal WRITE ▸ Math

Explain how you know that 0.27 = 27%.

LESSON 6

Fractions, Decimals, and Percents

LESSON AT A GLANCE

Common Core Standards

Understand decimal notation for fractions, and compare decimal fractions.
4.NF.C.6 Use decimal notation for fractions with denominators 10 or 100.

Understand ratio concepts and use ratio reasoning to solve problems.
6.RP.A.3c Use ratio and rate reasoning to solve real-world and mathematical problems, e.g., by reasoning about tables of equivalent ratios, tape diagrams, double number line diagrams,

or equations. Find a percent of a quantity as a rate per 100 (e.g., 30% of a quantity means 30/100 times the quantity); solve problems involving finding the whole, given a part and the percent.

Lesson Objective
Convert between fractions, decimals, and percents.

Materials
MathBoard

 Animated Math Models

---

1 TEACH and TALK • Animated Math Models

▶ **Unlock the Problem**

MATHEMATICAL PRACTICES

Help students understand how to convert between fractions, decimals, and percents.

Tell students that fractions, decimals, and percents are similar.

Draw a 10 × 10 grid on the board and shade 23 squares. Elicit from students that this quantity can be expressed as 23 out of 100, 23%, 23 hundredths, 0.23, or $\frac{23}{100}$.

Read the problem aloud. Help students see that the first step is to convert $\frac{2}{5}$ to an equivalent fraction with 100 in the denominator. Then, help them rename $\frac{40}{100}$ as 0.4, or 40%.

- **Look at Example A. What is the first step to convert $\frac{8}{25}$ into a decimal?** Find an equivalent fraction with 100 as the denominator. **How can you do this?** Multiply the numerator and denominator by 4 to get $\frac{32}{100}$.

Use Math Talk to focus on students' understanding of writing percents as decimals.

PG58 Planning Guide

Name _____

Fractions, Decimals, and Percents

Essential Question How can you convert between fractions, decimals, and percents?

🔑 Unlock the Problem

Every percent and decimal number can also be written as a fraction. All fractions can be written as decimals and percents. For example, $\frac{2}{5}$ of the songs in Bonnie's music collection are country songs. What percent of her song collection is country?

🔓 Write the percent that is equivalent to $\frac{2}{5}$.

STEP 1 Set up the equivalent fraction with a denominator of 100.

$$\frac{2 \times ?}{5 \times ?} = \frac{}{100}$$

STEP 2 Ask: By what factor can you multiply the denominator to get 100?

$$\frac{2 \times ?}{5 \times 20} = \frac{}{100} \longleftarrow \text{multiply the denominator by 20}$$

STEP 3 Multiply the numerator by the same factor, 20.

$$\frac{2 \times 20}{5 \times 20} = \frac{40}{100}$$

STEP 4 Write the fraction as a percent.

$$\frac{40}{100} = \underline{40} \text{ percent}$$

So, $\frac{2}{5}$ equals $\underline{40}$ percent.

💡 More Examples

A. Write $\frac{8}{25}$ as a decimal.

STEP 1 Write an equivalent fraction with a denominator of 100.

$$\frac{8 \times 4}{25 \times 4} = \frac{32}{100} \longleftarrow \text{multiply denominator and numerator by 4}$$

STEP 2 Write the fraction as a decimal.

$$\frac{32}{100} = 0.32$$

B. Write 90 percent as a fraction in simplest form.

STEP 1 Write 90% as a fraction.

$$90\% = \frac{90}{100}$$

STEP 2 Simplify.

$$90\% = \frac{90 \div 10}{100 \div 10} = \frac{9}{10}$$

Possible answer: Alike: Both have the same digits. Different: They have different values and 9% has a 0 in the tenths place.

Math Talk | **Mathematical Practices**
How are 9% and 90% alike when written as decimals? How are they different?

Getting Ready for Grade 6 GR11

GR: Practice, p. GRP6

Name _____ **Lesson 6**

Fractions, Decimals, and Percents

Write a decimal, a percent, or a simplified fraction.

1. $\frac{1}{4}$ as a percent — 25%
2. $\frac{7}{10}$ as a decimal — 0.70, or 0.7
3. $\frac{13}{20}$ as a percent — 65%
4. 25% as a fraction — $\frac{1}{4}$

5. $\frac{2}{5}$ as a percent — 40%
6. $\frac{9}{20}$ as a decimal — 0.45
7. $\frac{21}{50}$ as a percent — 42%
8. $\frac{1}{25}$ as a percent — 4%

9. 6% as a fraction — $\frac{3}{50}$
10. $\frac{3}{5}$ as a percent — 60%
11. $\frac{12}{25}$ as a decimal — 0.48
12. $\frac{3}{10}$ as a percent — 30%

13. $\frac{3}{4}$ as a percent — 75%
14. 65% as a fraction — $\frac{13}{20}$
15. $\frac{1}{5}$ as a percent — 20%
16. $\frac{9}{10}$ as a percent — 90%

Problem Solving

17. Ashlee has finished $\frac{7}{25}$ of her homework. What percent of the homework does Ashlee still need to finish? — 72%

18. Luz catches 83% of the balls in the outfield. What fraction of the balls does she not catch? — $\frac{17}{100}$

GRP6

GR: Reteach, p. GRR6

Name _____ Lesson 6 / Reteach

Fractions, Decimals, and Percents

You can write a percent and a decimal as a fraction. You can also write a fraction as a decimal and as a percent.

Write the percent that is equivalent to $\frac{17}{20}$.

Step 1 Set up the equivalent fraction with a denominator of 100.
$$\frac{17 \times ?}{20 \times ?} = \frac{}{100}$$

Step 2 Ask: By what factor can you multiply the denominator, 20, to get 100?
$$\frac{17 \times 5}{20 \times 5} = \frac{}{100} \longleftarrow \text{Multiply the denominator by 5.}$$

Step 3 Multiply the numerator by the same factor, 5.
$$\frac{17 \times 5}{20 \times 5} = \frac{85}{100}$$

Step 4 Write the fraction as a percent.
$$\frac{85}{100} = 85 \text{ percent}$$

So, $\frac{17}{20}$ equals 85%.

Write $\frac{7}{20}$ as a decimal.

Step 1 Write an equivalent fraction with a denominator of 100.
$$\frac{7 \times 5}{20 \times 5} = \frac{35}{100} \longleftarrow \text{Multiply the numerator and denominator by 5.}$$

Step 2 Write the fraction as a decimal.
$$\frac{35}{100} = 0.35$$

Write 15% as a fraction in simplest form.

Step 1 Write 15% as a fraction.
$$15\% = \frac{15}{100}$$

Step 2 Simplify.
$$15\% = \frac{15 \div 5}{100 \div 5} = \frac{3}{20}$$

Write a decimal, a percent, or a simplified fraction.

1. $\frac{1}{5}$ as a decimal — 0.20
2. $\frac{7}{10}$ as a percent — 70%
3. 60% as a fraction — $\frac{3}{5}$

Reteach / GRR6 / Grade 5

---

*GR – Getting Ready Lessons and Resources (www.thinkcentral.com)

Share and Show

Complete the steps to write $\frac{7}{20}$ as a percent.

1. By what factor should you multiply the denominator and numerator? **5**

$$\frac{7 \times ?}{20 \times ?} = \frac{?}{100}$$

2. For $\frac{7}{20}$, what is an equivalent fraction with a denominator of 100?

$$\frac{35}{100}$$

3. What percent is equivalent to $\frac{7}{20}$?

35%

Write a decimal, a percent, or a simplified fraction.

4. $\frac{1}{4}$ as a decimal

0.25

5. $\frac{3}{10}$ as a percent

30%

6. 80% as a fraction

$$\frac{4}{5}$$

On Your Own

Write a decimal, a percent, or a simplified fraction.

7. $\frac{1}{2}$ as a percent

50%

8. $\frac{9}{10}$ as a decimal

0.9, or 0.90

9. $\frac{11}{20}$ as a percent

55%

10. 75% as a fraction

$$\frac{3}{4}$$

11. $\frac{3}{5}$ as a percent

60%

12. $\frac{9}{25}$ as a decimal

0.36

13. $\frac{29}{50}$ as a percent

58%

14. $\frac{1}{20}$ as a percent

5%

15. 4% as fraction

$$\frac{1}{25}$$

16. $\frac{4}{5}$ as a percent

80%

17. $\frac{24}{25}$ as a decimal

0.96

18. $\frac{41}{50}$ as a percent

82%

Problem Solving

19. Whitney has finished $\frac{9}{20}$ of her book. What percent of the book does Whitney still need to read?

55%

20. Roger has completed $\frac{4}{25}$ of his math homework. What percent of his math homework does he still need to do?

84%

GR12

Getting Ready Lessons and Resources, pp. GR13–GR14 ✓ Checkpoint

Name _____

✓ Checkpoint

Concepts and Skills

Locate each number on the number line. Then complete the sentence.

1. $0.4, \frac{2}{5}, 0.35$

The number with the least value is **0.35**.

Write the numbers in order from least to greatest.

2. $0.4, \frac{3}{5}, 0.55, \frac{1}{4}$

$$\frac{1}{4}, 0.4, 0.55, \frac{3}{5}$$

3. $\frac{3}{4}, 0.7, \frac{1}{2}, 0.1$

$$0.1, \frac{1}{2}, 0.7, \frac{3}{4}$$

Use a factor tree to find the prime number factors.

4. 16 $2 \times 2 \times 2 \times 2$
5. 36 $2 \times 2 \times 3 \times 3$
6. 42 $2 \times 3 \times 7$

Write a decimal, a percent, or a simplified fraction.

7. 0.08 as a percent   **8%**
8. $\frac{3}{5}$ as a decimal   **0.6, or 0.60**
9. 80% as a fraction $\frac{4}{5}$
10. $\frac{13}{20}$ as a percent   **65%**

Problem Solving

For 11–12, use the data in the table.

11. What percent of the apes in the Wild Country Zoo are orangutans? **22%**

12. One species makes up 40% of the apes in the zoo. Which species is it? **chimpanzees**

Apes in the Wild Country Zoo	
Species	Number
Bonobo	4
Chimpanzee	20
Gorilla	15
Orangutan	11
Total	50

Getting Ready for Grade 6   GR13

Fill in the bubble or grid completely to show your answer.

13. Entries for the Lake Manatee Bass Fishing Contest are shown. First place is awarded to the contestant with the heaviest fish.

Lake Manatee Bass Contest	
Contestant	Weight of fish caught
George	6.25 pounds
Mia	6$\frac{2}{5}$ pounds
Harvey	6$\frac{1}{5}$ pounds

What is the correct order from first place to third place?

A First: George, Second: Mia, Third: Harvey
B First: Mia, Second: George, Third: Harvey
● First: Mia, Second: Harvey, Third: George
D First: Harvey, Second: Mia, Third: George

14. Ric used a factor tree to write 180 as a product of factors that are prime numbers. How many factors were in Ric's product?

A 2
B 3
● 4
D 5

15. On Monday, 6% of the students at Riverside School were absent. Written as a decimal, what portion of Riverside's students attended school that day?

A 0.06
B 0.6
● 0.94
D 9

16. The Hastings family drove $\frac{13}{25}$ of the distance to Yellowstone National Park on the first day of their vacation. What percent of the distance to the park remained for them to drive?

A 12%   C 48%
B 13%   ● 52%

GR14

---

2 PRACTICE

▶ Share and Show • Guided Practice

Remind students for each given fraction, they will need to first write an equivalent fraction with a denominator of 100 to write an equivalent decimal or percent.

▶ On Your Own • Independent Practice

Students should realize that once they write an equivalent fraction with 100 as the denominator, the numerator is used to write the percent.

▶ Problem Solving (Common Core) MATHEMATICAL PRACTICES

For Exercise 19, show students how to break the problem down into steps. One way is to first find the amount remaining ($\frac{11}{20}$) and then convert this number to a fraction with a denominator of 100, $\frac{55}{100}$. Then write this number as a percent (55%).

3 SUMMARIZE

(Common Core) MATHEMATICAL PRACTICES

Essential Question

How can you convert between fractions, decimals, and percents? Possible answer: To convert a fraction to a percent, write an equivalent fraction with a denominator of 100. Then I write the digits of the numerator followed by the percent symbol. To write a percent as a fraction, I take the digits in the front of the percent symbol and make them the numerator with a denominator of 100.

Math Journal   WRITE ▸ Math

Explain how to write $\frac{3}{10}$ as a decimal and as a percent.

LESSON 7

Divide Fractions by a Whole Number

LESSON AT A GLANCE

Common Core Standards
Apply and extend previous understandings of multiplication and division to multiply and divide fractions.
5.NF.B.7c Apply and extend previous understandings of division to divide unit fractions by whole numbers and whole numbers by unit fractions. Solve real world problems involving division of unit fractions by non-zero whole numbers and division of whole numbers by unit fractions, e.g., by using visual fraction models and equations to represent the problem.

Apply and extend previous understandings of multiplication and division to divide fractions by fractions.
6.NS.A.1 Interpret and compute quotients of fractions, and solve word problems involving division of fractions by fractions, e.g., by using visual fraction models and equations to represent the problem.

Lesson Objective
Divide a fraction by a whole number.

Materials
MathBoard

1 TEACH and TALK

▶ **Unlock the Problem**

MATHEMATICAL PRACTICES

Help students understand how the model represents the problem.

- **Explain what the model represents in Step 1.** The rectangle represents 1 quart of ice cream. It is divided into thirds and two of the thirds are shaded to represent $\frac{2}{3}$ of 1 quart.

- **Explain what the model represents in Step 2.** Possible answer: The thirds are divided into fourths to represent the amount each friend gets.

- **How do you know the answer is $\frac{1}{6}$?** Two of the 12 equal sections are shaded twice, and $\frac{2}{12} = \frac{1}{6}$.

Use **Math Talk** to focus on students' understanding of modeling division of fractions.

Try This!
- **Write a related multiplication problem to find $\frac{3}{4} \div 2$.** $\frac{3}{4} \div 2 = \frac{3}{4} \times \frac{1}{2} = \frac{3}{8}$

PG60 Planning Guide

This lesson builds on fraction and whole-number division presented in Chapter 8 and prepares students to divide fractions by fractions taught in Grade 6.

Name _____

Divide Fractions by a Whole Number
Essential Question How do you divide a fraction by a whole number?

🔑 Unlock the Problem (Real World)

Four friends share $\frac{2}{3}$ of a quart of ice cream equally. What fraction of a quart of ice cream does each friend get?

- What operation will you use to solve the problem?
  division

🔒 **Divide.** $\frac{2}{3} \div 4$

STEP 1
Let the rectangle represent 1 quart of ice cream. Divide it into thirds by drawing vertical lines. Shade 2 of the thirds.

STEP 2
Divide the rectangle into fourths by drawing horizontal lines. Shade $\frac{1}{4}$ of the $\frac{2}{3}$ already shaded.

STEP 3
The rectangle is now divided into **12** equal parts.
Each part is $\frac{1}{12}$ of the rectangle. Of the 12 equal parts, **2** parts are shaded twice. So, $\frac{2}{12}$, or $\frac{1}{6}$ of the rectangle is shaded twice.

So, each friend gets $\frac{2}{12}$, or $\frac{1}{6}$ of a quart of ice cream.

Possible expanation: The $\frac{2}{3}$ quart is being shared equally among 4 friends.

Math Talk **Mathematical Practices**
Explain why you divided the rectangle into fourths in Step 2.

Try This! Divide. $\frac{3}{4} \div 2$

STEP 1
Divide the rectangle into fourths. Shade 3 of the fourths.

STEP 2
Divide the rectangle into halves. Shade $\frac{1}{2}$ of the $\frac{3}{4}$ already shaded.

STEP 3
Of the 8 equal parts, $\frac{3}{8}$ parts are shaded twice. So, $\frac{3}{8}$ of the rectangle is shaded twice.

So, $\frac{3}{4} \div 2 = \frac{3}{8}$.

© Houghton Mifflin Harcourt Publishing Company

Getting Ready for Grade 6   GR15

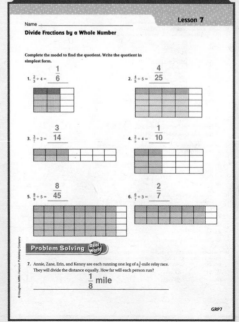

GR: Practice, p. GRP7

Name _____   Lesson 7
Divide Fractions by a Whole Number

Complete the model to find the quotient. Write the quotient in simplest form.

1. $\frac{1}{3} \div 4 = \frac{1}{6}$
2. $\frac{4}{5} \div 5 = \frac{4}{25}$
3. $\frac{1}{7} \div 2 = \frac{3}{14}$
4. $\frac{1}{2} \div 4 = \frac{1}{10}$
5. $\frac{8}{9} \div 5 = \frac{8}{45}$
6. $\frac{6}{7} \div 3 = \frac{2}{7}$

Problem Solving (Real World)

7. Annie, Zane, Erin, and Kenny are each running one leg of a $\frac{1}{2}$-mile relay race. They will divide the distance equally. How far will each person run?
$\frac{1}{8}$ mile

GRP7

GR: Reteach, p. GRR7

Name _____   Lesson 7
Reteach
Divide Fractions by a Whole Number

You can use a model to help you divide a fraction by a whole number.
Divide. $\frac{2}{5} \div 3$

Step 1 The denominator of the dividend is _5_. So divide a rectangle into five equal-size parts, or _fifths_. The numerator of the dividend is _2_. So shade _2_ of the fifths.

Step 2 The divisor is _3_. So divide the rectangle into _thirds_ by drawing horizontal lines. Shade $\frac{1}{3}$ of $\frac{2}{5}$.

Step 3 The rectangle is now divided into 15 equal parts. Each part is $\frac{1}{15}$ of the rectangle.

Step 4 Of the 15 equal parts, _2_ parts are shaded twice. So $\frac{2}{15}$ of the rectangle is shaded twice.
So $\frac{2}{5} \div 3 = \frac{2}{15}$.

Use the model to find the quotient. Write the quotient in simplest form.

1. $\frac{3}{4} \div 4 = \frac{3}{16}$
2. $\frac{1}{2} \div 3 = \frac{1}{6}$
3. $\frac{5}{6} \div 7 = \frac{5}{42}$
4. $\frac{4}{5} \div 3 = \frac{4}{15}$

Reteach   GRR7   Grade 5

*GR – Getting Ready Lessons and Resources (www.thinkcentral.com)

Share and Show

Complete the model to find the quotient. Write the quotient in simplest form.

1. $\frac{5}{6} \div 2 = \frac{5}{12}$

Divide the rectangle into sixths.
Shade 5 of the sixths.

Divide the rectangle into halves. Shade $\frac{1}{2}$ of $\frac{5}{6}$.

2. $\frac{3}{4} \div 3 = \frac{1}{4}$

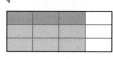

3. $\frac{2}{3} \div 3 = \frac{2}{9}$

4. $\frac{3}{5} \div 2 = \frac{3}{10}$

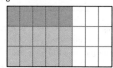

On Your Own

Complete the model to find the quotient. Write the quotient in simplest form.

5. $\frac{2}{5} \div 2 = \frac{1}{5}$

6. $\frac{5}{8} \div 3 = \frac{5}{24}$

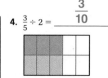

Draw a model to find the quotient. Write the quotient in simplest form.

Check students' models.

7. $\frac{4}{9} \div 2 = \frac{2}{9}$

8. $\frac{4}{5} \div 3 = \frac{4}{15}$

Problem Solving

9. Heather, Jocelyn, and Dane are each swimming one leg of a $\frac{9}{10}$ mile race. They will divide the distance equally. How far will each team member swim?

$\frac{3}{10}$ mile

GR16

2 **PRACTICE**

▶ **Share and Show •** **Guided Practice**

For Exercise 2, encourage students to plan their solution using the steps in Exercise 1 as a model. First, they should shade 3 of 4 fourths in one direction. Then they should shade 1 of 3 thirds in the other direction.

▶ **On Your Own •** **Independent Practice**

For Exercises 7–8, have students use a sheet of paper to draw a model to find the quotient. Before solving, have students describe the steps that they would take to draw a model to find the quotient for Exercise 7.

▶ **Problem Solving** Common Core **MATHEMATICAL PRACTICES**

Since there are 3 swimmers, students should model $\frac{9}{10} \div 3$ to solve the problem.

3 **SUMMARIZE**

Common Core **MATHEMATICAL PRACTICES**

Essential Question

How do you divide a fraction by a whole number? Possible answer: I would draw a rectangle, model the dividend by drawing and shading columns, and then divide the rectangle into the same number of rows as the number in the divisor. Then double shade that part of the dividend.

Math Journal WRITE ▶ Math

Explain how you can find the quotient $\frac{7}{8} \div 3$.

LESSON **8**

Ratios

LESSON AT A GLANCE

Common Core Standards

Develop understanding of fractions as numbers.
3.NF.A.1 Understand a fraction 1/*b* as the quantity formed by 1 part when a whole is partitioned into *b* equal parts; understand a fraction *a*/*b* as the quantity formed by *a* parts of size 1/*b*.

Understand ratio concepts and use ratio reasoning to solve problems.
6.RP.A.1 Understand the concept of a ratio and use

ratio language to describe a ratio relationship between two quantities.

Lesson Objective
Express real world quantities as ratios.

Vocabulary
ratio

Materials
MathBoard, two-color counters

GO DIGITAL

Animated Math Models

1 TEACH and TALK GO DIGITAL • Animated Math Models

▶ Unlock the Problem

MATHEMATICAL PRACTICES

Write the term *ratio* on the board. Tell students that a ratio is a comparison of two numbers. Distribute counters to students.

▶ Activity

Read the problem aloud. Have students show the ratio 3:2 with 3 yellow counters and 2 red counters.

Show students how to read the ratio from left to right. Help them say aloud, "The ratio of yellow counters to red counters is 3 to 2."

• **What is the ratio of red counters to yellow counters?** 2:3

Try This!

• Show 2 yellow counters and 5 red counters. Use the counters to show a ratio of red counters to the total number of counters. **What ratio can you write to represent this?** 5:7

• **Think about ratios in the real world that you could describe. What is the ratio of boys to girls in this classroom? What is the ratio of desks to chairs?** Answers will vary.

Use **Math Talk** to focus on students' understanding of ratios.

PG62 Planning Guide

Name _____

Ratios

Essential Question How can you express real world quantities as ratios?

🔑 Unlock the Problem (Real World)

Max sells bouquets of roses. There are 3 yellow roses and 2 red roses. What is the ratio of yellow to red roses?

A ratio is a comparison of two numbers.

> • A ratio is expressed by comparing one part to another, such as 4 feet to 20 toes, or 3 yellow roses to
> **2 red roses**

🔑 Activity Materials ■ two-color counters

Model the data.

STEP 1 Use 3 counters with the yellow side up to represent yellow roses and 2 counters with the red side up to represent red roses.

STEP 2 Write the ratio of yellow to red roses.
• Ratios can be written in different ways.
  3 to 2 or 3:2 or $\frac{3}{2}$ (as a fraction)

So, the ratio of yellow roses to red roses is __3 to 2__ , __3:2__ , or __$\frac{3}{2}$__ .

In the example above, you compared a part to a part. You can also use a ratio to compare a part to a whole or a whole to a part.

Try This! Show a ratio of red counters to total counters.

STEP 1 Count to find the number of red counters. __5__

STEP 2 Count to find the total number of counters. __7__

STEP 3 Write the ratio. __5 to 7, 5:7, $\frac{5}{7}$.__

The numbers would be reversed. The ratio would be 7 to 5, 7:5, or $\frac{7}{5}$.

Math Talk **Mathematical Practices**
How would the ratio change if you found the ratio of total counters to red counters?

© Houghton Mifflin Harcourt Publishing Company

Getting Ready for Grade 6 GR17

GR: Practice, p. GRP8

Name _____ Lesson 8
Ratios

For 1–3, use the drawing to write the ratio.
1. dark squares to light squares
   7 dark squares
   3 light squares __7 to 3__
2. light squares to total squares __3 to 10__
3. light squares to dark squares __3 to 7__

For 4–6, use the drawing to write the ratio.
4. total fruit to bananas __7 to 6__
5. apples to bananas __1 to 6__
6. apples to total fruit __1 to 7__

For 7–12, write the ratio.
7. weekend days to weekdays __2 to 5__
8. months in a year to months that start with a vowel __12 to 3__
9. months that start with F to months in a year __1 to 12__
10. vowels to consonants in *RATIO* __3 to 2__
11. vowels to letters in *MATHEMATICS* __4 to 11__
12. letters to consonants in *NUMBERS* __7 to 5__

Problem Solving (Real World)

13. Amanda has 15 coins in her pocket. Of these, 8 are quarters. What is the ratio of quarters to coins in Amanda's pocket? __8 to 15__

14. Michael has $0.50 in dimes in his pocket. He also has $0.20 in nickels in his pocket. What is the ratio of the number of dimes to nickels in Michael's pocket? __5 to 4__

GRP8

GR: Reteach, p. GRR8

Name _____ Lesson 8 Reteach
Ratios

A ratio compares two numbers.
Shawna is decorating a picture frame by repeating the tile pattern shown below.

What is the ratio of triangles to circles?

Step 1 Count the number of triangles and circles.
  triangles: __4__
  circles: __3__

Step 2 Use the numbers to write a ratio of triangles to circles. __4 to 3__

So, the ratio of triangles to circles is __4 to 3__.
You can also write this ratio as 4:3 and $\frac{4}{3}$.

Find the ratio of rectangles to circles.
1a. How many rectangles are there? __4__
1b. How many circles are there? __1__
1c. What is the ratio of rectangles to circles? __4 to 1__

Write the ratio. Students may write ratios in a different form.
2. dark circles to white circles __4 to 2__
3. total rectangles to light rectangles __5 to 4__

Reteach GRR8 Grade 5

***GR** – Getting Ready Lessons and Resources (www.thinkcentral.com)*

Share and Show

Find the ratio of red counters to yellow counters.

1a. How many red counters are there?

4

1b. How many yellow counters are there?

3

1c. What is the ratio of red to yellow counters?

4 to 3, 4:3, or $\frac{4}{3}$

Write the ratio.   Students may write ratios in a different form.

2. squares to circles

4 to 2

3. total squares to dark squares

9 to 7

On Your Own

Students may write ratios in a different form.

For 4–6, use the drawing to write the ratio.

4. dark to light

5 to 3

5. light to dark

3 to 5

6. light to total

3 to 8

For 7–9, use the drawing to write the ratio.

7. triangles to circles

5 to 4

8. dark to light

4 to 5

9. total shapes to circles

9 to 4

For 10–12, write the ratio.

10. weekdays to weekend days

5 to 2

11. weekend days to days in a week

2 to 7

12. days in a week to days in January

7 to 31

Problem Solving

13. The ratio of length to width in Gus's driveway is 13 yards to 4 yards. What is this ratio in feet? (Hint: 3 ft = 1 yd)

39 feet to 12 feet

GR18

② PRACTICE

▶ **Share and Show • Guided Practice**

Encourage students to say each ratio aloud, and reinforce the fact that they should read ratios from left to right.

▶ **On Your Own • Independent Practice**

Students may write the ratios for Exercises 4–12 in different ways. For example, the ratio of 4 to 3 can also be written as 4:3, or $\frac{4}{3}$.

▶ **Problem Solving** **MATHEMATICAL PRACTICES**

Have students draw a diagram of the driveway on a sheet of paper to help them solve the problem. Remind them to show their work as they convert yards to feet.

③ SUMMARIZE

MATHEMATICAL PRACTICES

Essential Question

How can you express real world quantities as ratios? Possible answer: A ratio of the number *a* to the number *b* can be expressed as *a* to *b*, $\frac{a}{b}$, or *a:b*. The positions of *a* and *b* are based on the order that they are compared.

Math Journal

Look at your classmates and write a ratio comparing the number of light-haired students to the total number of students. Now, write a ratio comparing the number of dark-haired students to the total number of students. What do you notice about the two ratios?

LESSON 9

Equivalent Ratios

LESSON AT A GLANCE

Common Core Standards
Extend understanding of fraction equivalence and ordering.
4.NF.A.1 Explain why a fraction *a/b* is equivalent to a fraction $(n \times a)/(n \times b)$ by using visual fraction models, with attention to how the number and size of the parts differ even though the two fractions themselves are the same size. Use this principle to recognize and generate equivalent fractions.

Understand ratio concepts and use ratio reasoning to solve problems.
6.RP.A.3a Use ratio and rate reasoning to solve real-world

and mathematical problems, e.g., by reasoning about tables of equivalent ratios, tape diagrams, double number line diagrams, or equations. Make tables of equivalent ratios relating quantities with whole-number measurements, find missing values in the tables, and plot the pairs of values on the coordinate plane. Use tables to compare ratios.

Lesson Objective
Determine if two ratios are equivalent.

Materials
MathBoard

 Animated Math Models

1 TEACH and TALK · Animated Math Models

▶ Unlock the Problem

MATHEMATICAL PRACTICES

Review the meanings of the terms *equivalent* and *ratio*. Tell students that an equivalent ratio is similar to an equivalent fraction—it is equal to the original ratio.

Read the problem aloud. Show students how to draw a diagram that represents the ratio 2:3. Then demonstrate how to use equivalent fractions to find the answer.

- **What factor can you multiply 3 by to get 12?** 4 **How can you use this information to solve the problem?** If you multiply the denominator by 4, then you have to multiply the numerator by 4.

- **What is the equivalent ratio?** The ratio 2 to 3 is equivalent to 8 to 12.

Try This!

- **Look at 6:8 and 18:24. What fraction do you get when you simplify $\frac{6}{8}$?** $\frac{3}{4}$ **What fraction do you get when you simplify $\frac{18}{24}$?** $\frac{3}{4}$ **How can you use this information to solve the problem?** If both ratios simplify to the same fraction, then they are equivalent.

PG64   Planning Guide

This lesson builds on writing equivalent fractions presented in Grade 4, and prepares students for writing equivalent ratios taught in Grade 6.

Name _____

Equivalent Ratios

Essential Question How can you determine if two ratios are equivalent?

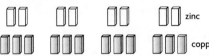 **Unlock the Problem** Real World

To make brass, you can mix 2 parts zinc to 3 parts copper, a ratio of 2 to 3. If you have 12 bars of copper and use them all, how many bars of zinc do you need to make brass?

Since ratios can be written as fractions, 2 to 3 can be written as $\frac{2}{3}$. Use what you know about equivalent fractions to find equivalent ratios.

🔑 **Use a diagram to find an equivalent ratio.**

STEP 1   Draw bars to represent a 2 to 3 ratio of zinc to copper.

STEP 2   Add groups until you have 12 bars of copper.

STEP 3   Count the zinc bars. Write an equivalent ratio.

There are 8 zinc bars. So, 2 to 3 is equivalent to the ratio 8 to 12.

- You know that each group of zinc to copper bars needed to make brass has a ratio of 2 to 3. How can you use this group to find an equivalent ratio?

Possible answer: Add equivalent groups. Since each group has the same ratio of 2 zinc bars to 3 copper bars, the sum will also have a 2 to 3 ratio.

Try This! Use equivalent ratios to find out if 6:8 is equivalent to 18:24.

STEP 1   Write the ratios as fractions.

$$6:8 = \frac{6}{8} \qquad 18:24 = \frac{18}{24}$$

STEP 2   Write the fractions in simplest form. Then compare.

$$\frac{6 \div 2}{8 \div 2} = \frac{3}{4} \qquad \frac{18 \div 6}{24 \div 6} = \frac{3}{4}$$

Both ratios equal $\frac{3}{4}$, so they are equivalent.

Possible answer: Ratios can be written as fractions. So, by writing the fractions in simplest form, I can compare them to see if they are equivalent.

Math Talk **Mathematical Practices**
How does knowing how to simplify fractions help you decide whether two ratios are equivalent?

Getting Ready for Grade 6   GR19

© Houghton Mifflin Harcourt Publishing Company

GR: Practice, p. GRP9

Name _____   Lesson 9
Equivalent Ratios

Write the equivalent ratio.

1. 8 to 20 = __4__ to 10   2. 6:5 = __42__ :35   3. 2 to 3 = 20 to __30__
$$\frac{8 \div 2}{20 \div 2} = \frac{4}{10}$$

4. 36:24 = 6:__4__   5. 6 to 9 = __18__ to 27   6. 64:72 = __8__ :9

7. 11 to 12 = 33 to __36__   8. 1:7 = __9__ :63   9. 21:57 = 7:__19__

Write *equivalent* or *not equivalent*.
10. 15:10 and 3:2   11. 24 to 16 and 8 to 4   12. 6:9 and 24:45
equivalent   not equivalent   not equivalent

13. 6:24 and 9:45   14. 15 to 20 and 3 to 4   15. 2:3 and 8:12
not equivalent   equivalent   equivalent

Problem Solving Real World

16. Are the ratios of free throws made to free throws attempted by the Rockets and by the Turbos equivalent?
no

Basketball Game Stats		
Team	Free Throws Made	Free Throws Attempted
Rockets	8	24
Turbos	16	36

17. In another game, the Rockets attempted only 12 free throws. If the ratio of free throws made to free throws attempted stays the same, how many free throws would you expect the team to make?
4 free throws

GRP9

GR: Reteach, p. GRR9

Name _____   Lesson 9
Reteach
Equivalent Ratios

Equivalent ratios are equal forms of the same ratio. You can use multiplication or division to write equivalent ratios.
Write the equivalent ratio.

4 to 7 = __?__ to 21
Step 1 Write the ratios as fractions.
$\frac{4}{7} = \frac{?}{21}$
Step 2 Compare the denominators.
$\frac{4}{7} = \frac{?}{21}$ Think: 21 > 7, so multiply.
Step 3 Multiply the numerator and denominator by the same number.
$\frac{4 \times 7}{7 \times 7} = \frac{?}{21}$ Think: 7 × 3 = 21, so multiply by 3.
$\frac{4 \times 3}{7 \times 3} = \frac{12}{21}$
So, 4 to 7 is equivalent to 12 to 21.

8 to 10 = 4 to __?__
Step 1 Write the ratios as fractions.
$\frac{8}{10} = \frac{4}{?}$
Step 2 Compare the numerators.
$\frac{8}{10} = \frac{4}{?}$ Think: 4 < 8, so divide.
Step 3 Divide the numerator and denominator by the same number.
$\frac{8 \div 2}{10 \div 2} = \frac{4}{?}$ Think: 8 ÷ 2 = 4, so divide by 2.
$\frac{8 \div 2}{10 \div 2} = \frac{4}{5}$
So, 8 to 10 is equivalent to 4 to 5.

Write *equivalent* or *not equivalent*.
1. 2 to 3 and 8 to 12   2. 15 to 20 and 3 to 5
equivalent   not equivalent
3. 5 to 6 and 25 to 36   4. 18 to 10 and 9 to 5
not equivalent   equivalent

Write the equivalent ratio.
5. 28 to 32 = __ to 8   6. 9 to 8 = 63 to __   7. 13:5 = __:15
7   56   39

Reteach   GRR9   Grade 5
© Houghton Mifflin Harcourt Publishing Company

*GR – Getting Ready Lessons and Resources (www.thinkcentral.com)

Share and Show

Are the ratios 3:5 and 12:20 equivalent?

1a. Write both ratios as fractions.
$$\frac{3}{5}, \frac{12}{20}$$

1b. Are both ratios in simplest form?
no

1c. Write both ratios in simplest form.
$$\frac{3}{5}, \frac{3}{5}$$

1d. Are the ratios equivalent?
yes

Write *equivalent* or *not equivalent*.

2. 1 to 3 and 2 to 6
equivalent

3. 3 to 7 and 12 to 21
not equivalent

On Your Own

Write the equivalent ratio.

4. 5 to 2 = **10** to 4

5. 3 to 6 = 7 to **14**

6. 7:2 = **21** :6

7. 14 to 21 = **10** to 15

8. 6:10 = **18** :30

9. 8 to 9 = 40 to **45**

Write *equivalent* or *not equivalent*.

10. 3:5 and 21:35
equivalent

11. 4 to 3 and 36 to 24
not equivalent

12. 27:72 and 9:24
equivalent

Problem Solving

13. Three of every 5 pizzas that Miggy's Pizza sells are cheese pizzas. Miggy's sold 80 pizzas today. How many of them would you expect were cheese?
48 pizzas

GR20

© Houghton Mifflin Harcourt Publishing Company

2 PRACTICE

▶ **Share and Show** • **Guided Practice**
Help students write out each ratio as fractions. Encourage them to use the terms *numerator*, *denominator*, *equivalent*, and *ratio* as they compare the ratios.

▶ **On Your Own** • **Independent Practice**
Students may need reminders to read each ratio from left to right in order to make sure they set up their equivalent fractions correctly.

▶ **Problem Solving** Common Core **MATHEMATICAL PRACTICES**
Have students work in small groups to draw diagrams that will help them solve the problem. Have students show the equivalent fractions that helped them find the correct answer.

3 SUMMARIZE

Common Core **MATHEMATICAL PRACTICES**

Essential Question
How can you determine if two ratios are equivalent? Possible answer: If two ratios written as fractions in simplest form are equal, then the two ratios are equivalent.

Math Journal WRITE ▶Math
A cookie recipe uses 2 cups of flour to make 60 cookies. Marlis needs to bake 180 cookies for a bake sale. How much flour will she need? Show your work.

Rates

LESSON AT A GLANCE

Common Core Standards
Extend understanding of fraction equivalence and ordering.
4.NF.A.1 Explain why a fraction a/b is equivalent to a fraction $(n \times a)/(n \times b)$ by using visual fraction models, with attention to how the number and size of the parts differ even though the two fractions themselves are the same size. Use this principle to recognize and generate equivalent fractions.

Understand ratio concepts and use ratio reasoning to solve problems.
6.RP.A.2 Understand the concept of a unit rate a/b associated with a ratio $a:b$ with $b \neq 0$, and use rate language in the context of a ratio relationship.

Lesson Objective
Find rates and unit rates.

Vocabulary
rate, unit rate

Materials
MathBoard

GO DIGITAL

☑ Animated Math Models

1 TEACH and TALK
GO DIGITAL • Animated Math Models

▶ **Unlock the Problem**

MATHEMATICAL PRACTICES

Review the meaning of a ratio by asking the students to give some examples of ratios. Then ask students if they have ever heard of the term rate. Have them give examples of a rate.
Possible answers: rate of speed, heart rate, rate of pay

Have students read the introductory paragraph.

- **How does a rate differ from a ratio?**
  Possible answer: A rate compares two quantities measured in different units.

- **How does a unit rate differ from a rate?**
  Possible answer: The second term in a unit rate is 1.

Have students read the problem.

- **What are the words in the problem that help you to write the rate?** 4 CDs for $12

- **How can you write the unit rate?**
  Possible answer: Write an equivalent fraction with a denominator of 1.

Use Math Talk to check students' understanding of rates and unit rates.

PG66 Planning Guide

This lesson builds on writing equivalent fractions presented in Grade 4, and prepares students for understanding unit rates taught in Grade 6.

Name _____

Rates

Essential Question How can you find rates and unit rates?

🔑 Unlock the Problem

CONNECT You know how to write ratios to compare two quantities. A **rate** is a ratio that compares two quantities that have different units of measure. A **unit rate** is a rate that has 1 unit as its second term.

Rafael is shopping at a used book and music store. A sign advertises 4 CDs for $12. What is the unit rate for the cost of 1 CD?

🔒 Write the rate in fraction form. Then find the unit rate.

STEP 1

Write the rate in fraction form to compare dollars to CDs.

$$\frac{\text{dollars}}{\text{CDs}} \longrightarrow \frac{12}{\boxed{4}}$$

STEP 2

Divide to find an equivalent rate so that 1 is the second term.

$$\frac{12}{4} = \frac{12 \div \boxed{4}}{4 \div \boxed{4}} = \frac{\boxed{3}}{1} \longleftarrow \text{unit rate}$$

So, the unit rate for CDs is $\boxed{\$3}$ for 1 CD.

- **What are the units of the quantities that are being compared?**
  dollars and CDs

- **What operations can you use to write equivalent ratios?**
  multiplication and division

No; Possible explanation: The unit rate is $\frac{1}{3}$ CD for $1; you cannot buy part of a CD.

Math Talk Mathematical Practices
Would it make sense to compare CDs to dollars to find a unit rate? **Explain.**

- **What if** the regular price of CDs is 5 for $20? What is the unit rate for CDs at the regular price? **Explain** how you found your answer.

$4 for 1 CD; Possible explanation: The rate is $\frac{20}{5}$. I divided the numerator and denominator by 5 to find the unit rate.

© Houghton Mifflin Harcourt Publishing Company

Getting Ready for Grade 6   GR21

GR: Practice, p. GRP10

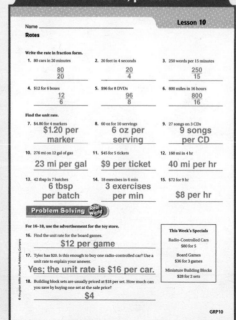

GR: Reteach, p. GRR10

*GR – Getting Ready Lessons and Resources (www.thinkcentral.com)

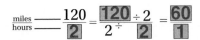 **Share and Show**

1. Find the unit rate of speed for 120 miles in 2 hours.

$$\frac{\text{miles}}{\text{hours}} \longrightarrow \frac{120}{2} = \frac{120 \div 2}{2 \div 2} = \frac{60}{1}$$

The unit rate of speed is ___60 miles___ per ___1 hour___.

Find the unit rate.

2. $5.00 for 2 T-shirts

$2.50 per T-shirt

3. 200 words in 4 min

50 words per min

4. 150 mi on 10 gal of gas

15 mi per gal

On Your Own

Write the rate in fraction form.

5. 90 words in 2 min

$$\frac{90}{2}$$

6. $1.20 for 6 goldfish

$$\frac{1.20}{6}$$

7. $0.05 per page

$$\frac{0.05}{1}$$

Find the unit rate.

8. $208 for 4 tires

$52 per tire

9. 300 mi per 15 gal

20 mi per gal

10. 240 people per 2 sq mi

120 people per sq mi

Problem Solving (Real World)

11. An ice skating rink charges $1.50 to rent ice skates for 30 minutes. What is the unit rate per hour for renting ice skates?

$3.00 per hour

GR22

2 PRACTICE

▶ **Share and Show • Guided Practice**

For Exercise 1, explain that the fraction bar can be read as the word *per* in a rate.

For Exercises 2–4, remind students to find the unit rate by writing an equivalent fraction with 1 in the denominator.

▶ **On Your Own • Independent Practice**

For Exercises 8–10, remind students to include the units of measure in the rate.

▶ **Problem Solving**  **MATHEMATICAL PRACTICES**

For Exercise 11, have students think about how many minutes equal an hour. Then ask them how they should find the rate in dollars per hour.

3 SUMMARIZE

 MATHEMATICAL PRACTICES

Essential Question

How can you find rates and unit rates?

Possible answer: I can write a rate as a ratio in fraction form. To find the unit rate, I can find an equivalent fraction with a denominator of 1.

Math Journal ✏ WRITE ▸Math

Explain how knowing a unit rate can help you determine other equivalent rates. Provide examples in your explanation.

LESSON 11

Distance, Rate, and Time

LESSON AT A GLANCE

Common Core Standards
Perform operations with multi-digit whole numbers and with decimals to hundredths.
5.NBT.B.6 Find whole-number quotients of whole numbers with up to four-digit dividends and two-digit divisors, using strategies based on place value, the properties of operations, and/or the relationship between multiplication and division. Illustrate and explain the calculation by using equations, rectangular arrays, and/or area models.

Understand ratio concepts and use ratio reasoning to solve problems.
6.RP.A.3b Use ratio and rate reasoning to solve real-world and mathematical problems, e.g., by reasoning about tables of equivalent ratios, tape diagrams, double number line diagrams, or equations. Solve unit rate problems including those involving unit pricing and constant speed.

Lesson Objective
Solve problems involving distance, rate, and time.

Materials
MathBoard

 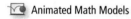
GO DIGITAL   Animated Math Models

1 TEACH and TALK   GO DIGITAL • Animated Math Models

▶ ## Unlock the Problem

Common Core **MATHEMATICAL PRACTICES**

Have students read the problem.

▶ ## Example 1

- **What is the question asking you to find: the distance, the rate, or the time?** time

- **Why do you divide to solve the problem?**
  Possible answer: I need to find the value of t, and division is the inverse operation of multiplication.

- **Why is $3\frac{1}{3}$ hours equivalent to 3 hours 20 minutes?** Possible answer: $\frac{1}{3}$ hour is $\frac{1}{3}$ of 60 minutes, which is 20 minutes.

▶ ## Example 2

- **What is the question asking you to find: the distance, the rate, or the time?** distance

- **Why do you multiply 120 by 2 to find the value of d?** Possible answer: The distance, d, is equal to the product of the rate (120) and the time (2).

PG68   Planning Guide

Name _____

Distance, Rate, and Time

Essential Question How can you solve problems involving distance, rate, and time?

🔑 Unlock the Problem Real World

You can use the formula $d = r \times t$ to solve problems involving distance, rate, and time. In the formula, d represents distance, r represents rate, and t represents time. The rate is usually a unit rate comparing distance to time, such as miles per hour.

- What word is used in place of rate?
  speed
- What are the given values?
  $d = 500$ and $r = 150$
- What is the unknown value?
  t, or time

🔒 Example 1

The winner of an automobile race drove 500 miles at an average speed of 150 miles per hour. How long did it take the winner to finish the race?

STEP 1
Write the formula.
$d = r \times t$

STEP 2
Replace d with 500 and r with 150.
$d = r \times t$
$500 = \boxed{150} \times t$

STEP 3
Use what you know about inverse operations to find t.
$500 \div \boxed{150} = t$
$3\frac{1}{3} = t$

So, it takes the winner $3\frac{1}{3}$ hours or 3 hours 20 minutes to complete the race.

🔒 Example 2

A race car driver traveled at an average speed of 120 miles per hour to finish a race in 2 hours. What was the length of the race?

Possible answer: In Example 1, the missing value is a factor, so the inverse operation, division, must be used to find its value. In Example 2, the missing value is the product, which can be found using multiplication.

STEP 1
Write the formula.
$d = r \times t$

STEP 2
Replace r with 120 and t with 2.
$d = r \times t$
$d = \boxed{120} \times \boxed{2}$

STEP 3
Multiply to solve for d.
$d = 120 \times 2$
$d = \boxed{240}$

So, the race was 240 miles long.

Math Talk **Mathematical Practices**
Why were different operations used in Step 3 of Examples 1 and 2?

See above.

© Houghton Mifflin Harcourt Publishing Company

Getting Ready for Grade 6   GR23

This lesson builds on division concepts presented in Chapter 2 and prepares students for solving distance, rate, and time problems taught in Grade 6.

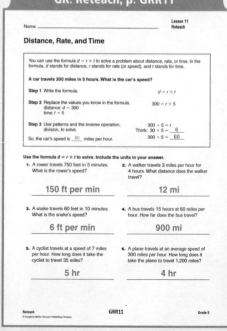

GR: Practice, p. GRP11

Name _____   Lesson 11
Distance, Rate, and Time

Use the formula $d = r \times t$ to solve. Include the unit in your answer.

1. A truck continuously travels at an average speed of 60 miles per hour. How long does it take the truck to travel 240 miles?
$d = r \times t$
$240 = 60 \times t$
$240 \div 60 = t$
$4 = t$
4 hr

2. A boat travels 3,600 meters in 12 minutes. What is the boat's speed?
300 m per min

3. A cyclist travels 7 hours at a speed of 11 miles per hour. How far does the cyclist travel?
77 mi

4. $d = 300$ cm
$r = 2$ cm per min
$t = $ **150 min**

5. $d = $ **270 mi**
$r = 45$ mi per hr
$t = 6$ hr

6. $d = 400$ yd
$r = $ **20 yd per min**
$t = 20$ min

7. $d = $ **1,200 mi**
$r = 120$ mi per hr
$t = 10$ hr

8. $d = 700$ ft
$r = $ **14 ft per min**
$t = 50$ min

9. $d = 1,200$ mi
$r = 600$ mi per hr
$t = $ **2 hr**

Problem Solving Real World

Use the road signs and the formula. $d = r \times t$

10. How long will it take a car traveling the speed limit to reach Crestview?
3 hr

SPEED LIMIT 65 mph   SPEED LIMIT 65 mph
Crestview 195 mi   Oceanside 230 mi

11. A car travels the speed limit. Can it reach Oceanside in 4 hours? Explain.
Yes; Possible explanation: The car can travel 260 miles in 4 hours, and 230 < 260.

GRP11

GR: Reteach, p. GRR11

Name _____   Lesson 11
Reteach

Distance, Rate, and Time

You can use the formula $d = r \times t$ to solve a problem about distance, rate, or time. In the formula, d stands for distance, r stands for rate (or speed), and t stands for time.

A car travels 300 miles in 5 hours. What is the car's speed?

Step 1 Write the formula. $d = r \times t$

Step 2 Replace the values you know in the formula.
distance: $d = 300$ $300 = r \times 5$
time: $t = 5$

Step 3 Use patterns and the inverse operation, division, to solve.
$300 \div 5 = r$
Think: $30 \div 5 = \underline{6}$ $300 \div 5 = \underline{60}$

So, the car's speed is $\underline{60}$ miles per hour.

Use the formula $d = r \times t$ to solve. Include the units in your answer.

1. A rower travels 750 feet in 5 minutes. What is the rower's speed?
150 ft per min

2. A walker travels 3 miles per hour for 4 hours. What distance does the walker travel?
12 mi

3. A snake travels 60 feet in 10 minutes. What is the snake's speed?
6 ft per min

4. A bus travels 15 hours at 60 miles per hour. How far does the bus travel?
900 mi

5. A cyclist travels at a speed of 7 miles per hour. How long does it take the cyclist to travel 35 miles?
5 hr

6. A plane travels at an average speed of 300 miles per hour. How long does it take the plane to travel 1,200 miles?
4 hr

Reteach   GRR11   Grade 5
© Houghton Mifflin Harcourt Publishing Company

*GR – Getting Ready Lessons and Resources (www.thinkcentral.com)

Share and Show

1. A cyclist travels 45 miles in 3 hours. What is the cyclist's speed?

Write the formula: $d = \boxed{r} \times \boxed{t}$

Replace d with $\underline{45}$.

Replace t with $\underline{3}$.

The rate is $\underline{15}$ miles per hour.

Use the formula $d = r \times t$ to solve. Include the units in your answer.

2. A train travels at an average speed of 80 miles per hour for 5 hours. How far does the train travel?

400 miles

3. A horse travels at an average speed of 12 miles per hour. How long does it take the horse to travel 60 miles?

5 hours

On Your Own

Use the formula $d = r \times t$ to solve. Include the unit in your answer.

4. A hiker travels at a speed of 3 miles per hour for 3 hours. How far does the hiker travel in that time?

9 miles

5. A snail travels at a speed of 2 centimeters per minute. How long does the snail take to travel 30 centimeters?

15 minutes

6. A boat travels 6 miles in 24 minutes. What is the average speed of the boat?

$\frac{1}{4}$ **mile per minute**

7. $d = 320$ cm

$r = \dfrac{40 \text{ cm per}}{\text{sec}}$

$t = 8$ sec

8. $d = \mathbf{300\ km}$

$r = 50$ km per hr

$t = 6$ hr

9. $d = 150$ ft

$r = 20$ ft per min

$t = 7\frac{1}{2}$ **min or 7.5 min**

Problem Solving

10. In an experiment, Ava found that it took a ball 5 seconds to roll down an 80-foot ramp. What is the average speed of the ball?

16 feet per second

11. Jason's family is driving 1,375 miles to Grand Canyon National Park. They plan to drive at an average speed of 55 miles per hour. How long will they be driving to reach the park?

25 hours

GR24

© Houghton Mifflin Harcourt Publishing Company

---

2 PRACTICE

▶ **Share and Show • Guided Practice**

For Exercises 1–3, remind students that the speed is the rate.

▶ **On Your Own • Independent Practice**

For Exercise 6, make sure students use 6 for the distance and 24 for the time. This will result in an answer that is a fraction.

▶ **Problem Solving** Common Core **MATHEMATICAL PRACTICES**

For Exercises 10 and 11, remind students to identify the known information as distance, rate, or time before replacing the variables with given values into the formula.

3 SUMMARIZE

Common Core **MATHEMATICAL PRACTICES**

Essential Question

How can you solve problems involving distance, rate, and time? Possible answer: I can use the formula, $d = r \times t$. I replace the variables in the formula with the known values and solve to find the unknown value.

Math Journal WRITE ▶Math

Write a word problem involving distance, rate, and time. Explain how to solve your problem.

Getting Ready Lessons and Resources, pp. GR25–GR26 ✔ **Checkpoint**

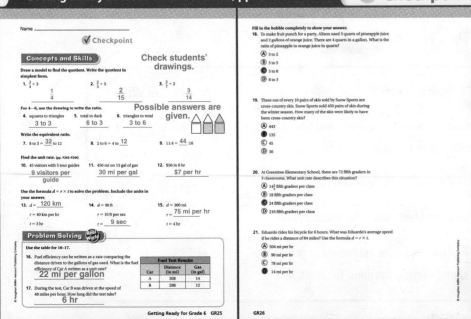

Summative Assessment

Use the **Getting Ready Test** to assess students' progress in Getting Ready for Grade 6 Lessons 1–11.

Getting Ready Tests are provided in multiple-choice and mixed-response format in the *Getting Ready Lessons and Resources.*

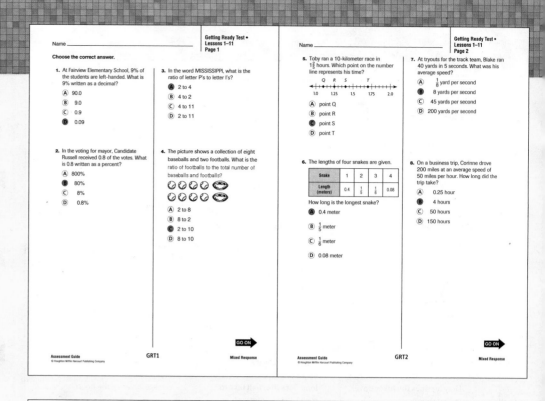

Getting Ready Test is available online.

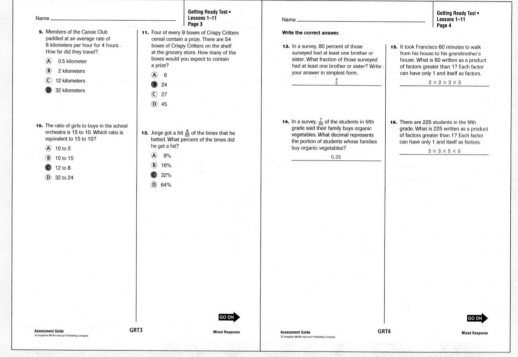

✔️ Data-Driven Decision Making 🔺RtI

Item	Lesson	Common Error	Intervene With
1, 2	5	May not understand the relationship between decimals and percents	R—GRR5
3, 4	8	May not understand the relationship between the parts of a quantity and the whole of a quantity	R—GRR8
5, 6	2	May not understand how to find and compare decimals, fractions, and mixed numbers	R—GRR2
7, 8, 9	11	May not understand how to solve problems involving distance, rate, and time	R—GRR11
10, 11	9	May not understand how to find ratios that are equivalent to given ratios	R—GRR9
12, 13, 14	6	May not understand how to convert among fractions, decimals, and percents	R—GRR6

Key: R—Getting Ready Lessons and Resources: Reteach

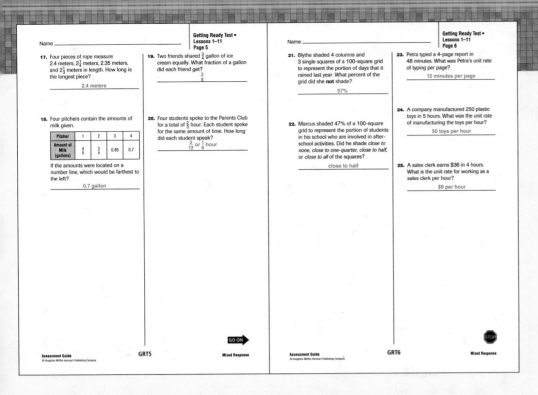

GO ON

Portfolio Suggestions The portfolio represents the growth, talents, achievements, and reflections of the mathematics learner. Students might spend a short time selecting work samples for their portfolios.

You may want to have students respond to the following questions:

- What new understanding of math have I developed in the past several weeks?
- What growth in understanding or skills can I see in my work?
- What can I do to improve my understanding of math ideas?
- What would I like to learn more about?

For information about how to organize, share, and evaluate portfolios, see the *Chapter Resources*.

✓ Data-Driven Decision Making ▲RtI

Item	Lesson	Common Error	Intervene With
15, 16	3	May not understand what a factor is and how to find the factors of a given number	R—GRR3
17, 18	1	May not understand how to compare fractions, decimals, and percents	R—GRR1
19, 20	7	May not understand how to divide a fraction by a whole number	R—GRR7
21, 22	4	May not understand how to express real-world quantities as percents	R—GRR4
23, 24, 25	10	May not understand how to find a unit rate, given a rate	R—GRR10

Key: R—Getting Ready Lessons and Resources: Reteach

LESSON 12

Understand Integers

LESSON AT A GLANCE

Common Core Standards
Graph points on the coordinate plane to solve real-world and mathematical problems.
5.G.A.1 Use a pair of perpendicular number lines, called axes, to define a coordinate system, with the intersection of the lines (the origin) arranged to coincide with the 0 on each line and a given point in the plane located by using an ordered pair of numbers, called its coordinates. Understand that the first number indicates how far to travel from the origin in the direction of one axis, and the second number indicates how far to travel in the direction of the second axis, with the convention that the names of the two axes and the coordinates correspond (e.g., *x*-axis and *x*-coordinate, *y*-axis and *y*-coordinate).

Apply and extend previous understandings of numbers to the system of rational numbers.
6.NS.C.5 Understand that positive and negative numbers are used together to describe quantities having opposite directions or values (e.g., temperature above/below zero, elevation above/below sea level, credits/debits, positive/negative electric charge); use positive and negative numbers to represent quantities in real-world contexts, explaining the meaning of 0 in each situation.

Lesson Objective
Understand positive and negative numbers, and use them to represent real world quantities.

Vocabulary
integer, opposite

Materials
MathBoard

GO DIGITAL

☑ Animated Math Models

---

1 TEACH and TALK
GO DIGITAL • Animated Math Models

▶ **Unlock the Problem**

MATHEMATICAL PRACTICES

Have students read the opening paragraph. Discuss the new vocabulary.

- **What is the opposite of ⁻2? Explain.** 2; Possible explanation: On a number line integers that are opposite are the same distance from 0. ⁻2 is 2 units to left of 0, so the opposite is 2 units to the right of 0, ⁺2 or 2.

- **Are there any integers between 0 and 1? Explain.** No. Possible explanation: There are no numbers between 0 and 1 that are whole numbers or their opposites.

PG72 Planning Guide

This lesson builds on understanding the composition of the number line presented in Chapters 1 and 9, and prepares students for integers taught in Grade 6.

Name _____

Understand Integers

Essential Question How can you use positive and negative numbers to represent real world quantities?

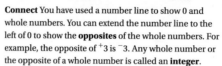**Unlock the Problem** *Real World*

Connect You have used a number line to show 0 and whole numbers. You can extend the number line to the left of 0 to show the **opposites** of the whole numbers. For example, the opposite of ⁺3 is ⁻3. Any whole number or the opposite of a whole number is called an **integer**.

negative integers ←——|——→ positive integers

⁻4 ⁻3 ⁻2 ⁻1 0 ⁺1 ⁺2 ⁺3 ⁺4

Negative integers are written with a negative sign, ⁻. Positive integers are written with or without a positive sign, ⁺.

- How can you tell whether a number is an integer or not?
Possible answer: It is an integer if it is a whole number or the opposite of a whole number.

Example 1

The temperature in Fairbanks, Alaska, was 37 degrees below zero. Write an integer to represent the situation.

STEP 1 Decide whether the integer is positive or negative.
The word ___**below**___ tells me that the integer is ___**negative**___.

STEP 2 Write the integer: ___⁻37___

So, the temperature in Fairbanks was ___⁻37___ degrees.

Example 2

The Koala Bears gained 11 yards on a football play. Write an integer to represent the situation. Then, tell what 0 represents in that situation.

STEP 1 Decide what positive integers and negative integers represent.
Positive integers represent yards ___**gained**___.
Negative integers represent yards ___**lost**___.

STEP 2 Decide what 0 represents.
So, 0 means yards were neither ___**gained**___
nor ___**lost**___.

Possible answers: below, less than, lost, before, under

Math Talk **Mathematical Practices**
Identify some words that might tell you that an integer is negative.

Getting Ready for Grade 6   GR27

GR: Practice, p. GRP12

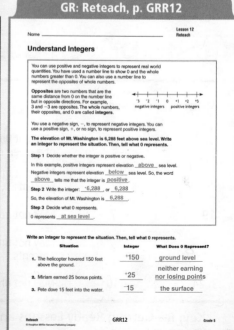

Name _____ **Lesson 12**
Understand Integers

Write an integer to represent the situation.

1. 5 degrees below zero ⁻5
2. a profit of $37 ⁺37
3. an altitude of 1,384 feet ⁺1384
4. a loss of 12 points ⁻12
5. a gain of 15 yards ⁺15
6. $50 in debt ⁻50

Write an integer to represent the situation. Then, tell what 0 represents.

Situation	Integer	What Does 0 Represent?
7. Trisha earned $18 babysitting.	⁺18	neither earning nor losing money
8. Luis read 5 more books.	⁺5	read the same number of books
9. The submarine is 2,500 feet below sea level.	⁻2,500	sea level
10. Lexi lost $10.	⁻10	neither losing nor gaining money

Problem Solving *Real World*

11. Zachary deposited $125 into his savings account. What integer can you write to represent the deposit? What does 0 represent?
⁺125; neither depositing nor withdrawing any money

12. Hannah dives 25 feet below sea level. What integer can you write to represent how far she dives? What does 0 represent?
⁻25; sea level

GRP12

GR: Reteach, p. GRR12

Name _____ Lesson 12 Reteach
Understand Integers

You can use positive and negative integers to represent real world quantities. You have used a number line to show 0 and the whole numbers greater than 0. You can also use a number line to represent the opposites of whole numbers.

Opposites are two numbers that are the same distance from 0 on the number line but in opposite directions. For example, 3 and ⁻3 are opposites. The whole numbers, their opposites, and 0 are called **integers**.

⁻3 ⁻2 ⁻1 0 ⁺1 ⁺2 ⁺3
negative integers   positive integers

You use a negative sign, ⁻, to represent negative integers. You can use a positive sign, ⁺, or no sign, to represent positive integers.

The elevation of Mt. Washington is 6,288 feet above sea level. Write an integer to represent the situation. Then, tell what 0 represents.

Step 1 Decide whether the integer is positive or negative.
In this example, positive integers represent elevation ___above___ sea level. Negative integers represent elevation ___below___ sea level. So, the word ___above___ tells me that the integer is ___positive___.

Step 2 Write the integer: ___⁺6,288___, or ___6,288___.
So, the elevation of Mt. Washington is ___6,288___.

Step 3 Decide what 0 represents.
0 represents ___at sea level___.

Write an integer to represent the situation. Then, tell what 0 represents.

Situation	Integer	What Does 0 Represent?
1. The helicopter hovered 150 feet above the ground.	⁺150	ground level
2. Miriam earned 25 bonus points.	⁺25	neither earning nor losing points
3. Pete dove 15 feet into the water.	⁻15	the surface

Reteach GRR12 Grade 5

*GR – Getting Ready Lessons and Resources (*www.thinkcentral.com*)

Share and Show

Write an integer to represent the situation.

1. a loss of $25

   The word *loss* represents an integer that is
   negative .

   The integer that represents the situation
   is **$^-25$** .

2. 73 degrees above zero **$^+73$**

3. 200 feet below sea level **$^-200$**

4. a profit of $76 **$^+76$**

Write an integer to represent the situation. Then, tell what 0 represents.

Situation	Integer	What Does 0 Represent?
5. The passenger jet flew at an altitude of 34,000 feet.	$^+34,000$	sea level
6. Zack lost 45 points on his first turn.	$^-45$	neither gaining nor losing points
7. Craig was 20 minutes early for his appointment.	$^-20$	on time for the appointment

On Your Own

Write an integer to represent the situation.

8. the temperature went up 2 degrees **$^+2$**

9. 11 feet below sea level **$^-11$**

10. an increase of 37 students **$^+37$**

11. 15 seconds before rocket liftoff **$^-15$**

Write an integer to represent the situation. Then, tell what 0 represents.

Situation	Integer	What Does 0 Represent?
12. Amelia earned $1,200 in one week.	$^+1,200$	neither earning nor losing money
13. The coal was 2 miles below ground level.	$^-2$	ground level
14. The alarm clock rang 5 minutes early.	$^-5$	the alarm ringing on time

Problem Solving

15. Gina withdrew $600 from her checking account to pay for her new guitar. What integer can you write to represent the withdrawal? What does 0 represent?

    $^-600$; neither withdrawing nor depositing money in her checking acount

GR28

► ## Example 1

- **What is the opposite of 37 degrees below zero?** 37 degrees above zero

► ## Example 2

- **How could you use an integer to represent 11 yards lost?** $^-11$

2 PRACTICE

► ### Share and Show • Guided Practice

For Exercise 4, help students to see that a "profit" is a gain in the amount of money you have. So, as with a gain of 11 yards on a football play, it is represented by a positive integer.

► ### On Your Own • Independent Practice

If students have difficulty with Exercises 12–14, encourage them to look for words that suggest integers and then to think of the opposites of those words. For Exercise 13, "below ground level" suggests a negative integer. The opposite is "above ground level." Zero represents what is between above ground level and below ground level, namely, ground level itself.

► ## Problem Solving

You may wish to explain that "withdrawing" money from a checking account is taking money *out of* the account. Since this decreases the amount in the account, the withdrawal is represented by a negative integer.

3 SUMMARIZE

 MATHEMATICAL PRACTICES

Essential Question

How can you use positive and negative numbers to represent real world quantities?

Possible answer: Decide whether the quantity is best represented as positive or negative. Then write the integer with the appropriate positive or negative sign.

Math Journal ✏ WRITE ▸ *Math*

Make a list of words that suggest positive real world quantities and a list of words that suggest negative real world quantities.

Getting Ready for Grade 6 Lesson 12   PG73

LESSON 13

Algebra • Write and Evaluate Expressions

LESSON AT A GLANCE

Common Core Standards

Write and interpret numerical expressions.

5.OA.A.2 Write simple expressions that record calculations with numbers, and interpret numerical expressions without evaluating them.

Apply and extend previous understandings of arithmetic to algebraic expressions.

6.EE.A.2c Write, read, and evaluate expressions in which letters stand for numbers. Evaluate expressions at specific values of their variables. Include expressions that arise from formulas used in real-world problems. Perform arithmetic operations, including those involving whole-number exponents, in the conventional order when there are no parentheses to specify a particular order (Order of Operations).

Lesson Objective
Write and evaluate expressions.

Materials
MathBoard

Animated Math Models
HMH Mega Math

---

1 TEACH and TALK

GO DIGITAL • **Animated Math Models**

▶ Unlock the Problem

MATHEMATICAL PRACTICES

Tell students that an *expression* is a series of numbers, variables, and operations that describe a value.

Read the first problem aloud. Help students see how $5 + c$ relates to the word description, and show them how they can replace the variable with a number in order to evaluate the expression.

Try This!

- **If the tools cost $18, how can you find out how much Montel will pay?** add 5 **What is the expression?** $5 + 18$

- **Write an example of an expression for *x*.** Answers will vary. **How can you evaluate the expression if *x* = 2?** Possible answer: I will replace *x* in my expression with 2 and then evaluate the expression by performing the operation in the expression.

PG74 Planning Guide

Name _____

Write and Evaluate Expressions

Essential Question How can you write and evaluate expressions?

This lesson builds on writing and evaluating numerical expressions presented in Chapter 1 and prepares students for writing and evaluating algebraic expressions in Grade 6.

Unlock the Problem (Real World)

Montel hires Shea to buy some tools for him at the hardware store. Montel will pay Shea $5 more than the cost of the tools she buys.

A. How can you represent this payment as an expression?

B. How can you use the expression to calculate what Montel will pay Shea?

🔑 **Write an expression for what Montel will pay.**

STEP 1 Choose a variable and explain what it stands for.

Let *c* equal the cost of the tools.

STEP 2 Write a word expression.

$5 more than the cost.

STEP 3 Replace the word expression with an addition expression using *c*.

$5 + c$

So, an expression that tells how much Montel owes Shea is

$5 + c$.

- The problem states that Montel will pay $5 *more than cost*. What operation do the words *more than* suggest?

addition

5 dollars more than the cost

$5 + c$

Try This! If the tools cost a total of $18, how much will Montel pay Shea? Evaluate the expression $5 + c$ for $c = 18$.

STEP 1 Write the expression. $5 + c$

STEP 2 Replace *c* with __18__. $5 + 18$

STEP 3 Add to evaluate. $5 + 18 = 23$

So, Montel will pay Shea __$23__.

Math Talk **Mathematical Practices**

What key words might tell you that you need to use addition in a word problem?

Possible answers: more than, plus, greater than, in all, total, altogether

Getting Ready for Grade 6   GR29

GR: Practice, p. GRP13

Name _____

ALGEBRA Lesson 13

Write and Evaluate Expressions

Write an expression.

1. Rosie has some charms, *c*, for her charm bracelet. Ray gives Rosie 3 new charms. How many charms does Rosie have now?

$c + 3$

2. Grayson has some model cars, *m*. He loses 2 of them. How many model cars does Grayson have now?

$m - 2$

3. Margo has 60 party favors that she wants to share equally with her guests, *g*. How many party favors will each guest get?

$60 \div g$

4. Phillip earns $10 each hour he works, *h*. How much does Phillip earn?

$10 \times h$

Evaluate each expression for the value given.

5. $t - 14$ for $t = 27$ **13**

6. $32 + m$ for $m = 17$ **49**

7. $y \times 7$ for $y = 14$ **98**

8. $w \times 8$ for $w = 18$ **144**

9. $125 \div n$ for $n = 25$ **5**

10. $b - 35$ for $b = 93$ **58**

11. $c \times 9$ for $c = 13$ **117**

12. $d \div 12$ for $d = 72$ **6**

13. $f + 0$ for $f = 17$ **17**

Problem Solving (Real World)

14. Kacey is 2 years younger than her sister. If *y* represents her sister's age, what expression can you write that represents Kacey's age? How old is Kacey if her sister is 14 years old?

$y - 2$; 12 years old

15. Greenville gets 3 more inches of snow than Charlotte gets. If *s* represents the number of inches of snow that Charlotte gets, what expression can you write that represents the amount of snow Greenville gets? How much snow does Greenville get if Charlotte gets 5 inches?

$s + 3$; 8 inches

GRP13

GR: Reteach, p. GRR13

Name _____

Lesson 13 Reteach

Algebra • Write and Evaluate Expressions

An **expression** is a mathematical phrase made up of numbers, variables, and operation symbols. A **variable** is a symbol that represents one or more numbers. You evaluate an expression by replacing each variable with a number and simplifying.

Maura sells handmade soap at the farmers' market for $4.00 per bar.

- Write an expression for how much Maura earns selling bars of soap.
- Evaluate the expression to determine how much money she will earn if she sells 26 bars of soap.

Step 1 Choose a variable and explain what it stands for.	Let *s* = the number of bars of soap Maura sells.
Step 2 Write a word expression.	$4 earned for each bar of soap sold
Step 3 Replace the word expression with a multiplication expression using *s*.	$4 \times s$
Step 4 Replace *s* with 26.	4×26
Step 5 Multiply to evaluate.	$4 \times 26 = 104$

So, Maura will earn $104 if she sells 26 bars of soap.

Write an expression.

1. Jack's dog weighs *p* pounds and his puppy weighs 15 pounds less. How much does the puppy weigh?

$p - 15$

2. Paul saved *d* dollars. Sally saved $25 more than Paul saved. How much did Sally save?

$d + 25$

Evaluate each expression for the value given.

3. $n - 17$ for $n = 50$ **33**

4. $27 + t$ for $t = 30$ **57**

5. $g \times 15$ for $g = 7$ **105**

6. $88 \div p$ for $p = 4$ **22**

Reteach   GRR13   Grade 5

---

*GR – Getting Ready Lessons and Resources (www.thinkcentral.com)

Share and Show

Write an expression.
Tallahassee's temperature is 15 degrees less than the temperature in Miami.

1a. What operation does the phrase *less than* suggest?

subtraction

1b. Write a word expression:
Possible answer: 15° less than the Miami temperature

1c. Write an expression for Tallahassee's temperature. Let m stand for the temperature in Miami.

$m - 15$

1d. Evaluate the expression for Tallahassee's temperature for $m = 90$.

75

Evaluate each expression for the value given.

2. $b - 45$ for $b = 70$
25

3. $13 + a$ for $a = 40$
53

On Your Own

Write an expression.

4. Zeke has some tropical fish, f. Dean gave Zeke 5 new fish. How many fish does Zeke have now?

$f + 5$

5. Myra had some candles, c. She used up 12 of them. How many candles does Myra have now?

$c - 12$

Evaluate each expression for the value given.

6. $s - 18$ for $s = 80$
62

7. $49 + k$ for $k = 31$
80

8. $w \times 6$ for $w = 13$
78

9. $60 \div n$ for $n = 20$
3

10. $t \times 12$ for $t = 8$
96

11. $r - 25$ for $r = 110$
85

Problem Solving (Real World)

12. Keith is 2 inches shorter than his sister. If s represents his sister's height, what expression can you write that represents Keith's height?

Possible answer: $s - 2$

GR30

© Houghton Mifflin Harcourt Publishing Company

2 PRACTICE

▶ **Share and Show • Guided Practice**

For Exercise 1, work with students to write the word description as an expression with variables.

▶ **On Your Own • Independent Practice**

For Exercises 6–11, encourage students to write out the steps to evaluate an expression as they replace the variable with a value in the expression.

▶ **Problem Solving** (Common Core) **MATHEMATICAL PRACTICES**

Encourage students to draw and label a diagram that relates Keith and his sister's height.

3 SUMMARIZE

(Common Core) **MATHEMATICAL PRACTICES**

Essential Question

How can you write and evaluate expressions?

Possible answer: Write an expression that matches the word description. Replace the variable with a given value and evaluate the expression.

Math Journal **WRITE** ▸ *Math*

Explain how to evaluate the expression $40 \div c$ for $c = 8$.

LESSON 14

Algebra • Understand Inequalities

LESSON AT A GLANCE

Common Core Standards
Understand the place value system.
5.NBT.A.3b Read, write, and compare decimals to thousandths. Compare two decimals to thousandths based on meanings of the digits in each place, using $>$, $=$, and $<$ symbols to record the results of comparisons.

Reason about and solve one-variable equations and inequalities.
6.EE.B.8 Write an inequality of the form $x > c$ or $x < c$ to represent a constraint or condition in a real-world or mathematical problem. Recognize that inequalities of the form $x > c$ or $x < c$ have infinitely many solutions; represent solutions of such inequalities on number line diagrams.

Lesson Objective
Understand inequalities and use them to solve problems.

Materials
MathBoard, Number Lines (see *eTeacher Resources*)

1 TEACH and TALK

▶ ### Unlock the Problem

MATHEMATICAL PRACTICES

Write the word *inequality* on the board. Point out the root word, *equal*. Tell students that an inequality compares two unequal quantities.

Review the symbols $<$ (less than), $>$ (greater than), $\leq$ (less than or equal to) and $\geq$ (greater than or equal to).

Write the expression $c > 7$ on the board. Help students read it aloud as "*c* is greater than 7." Point out that the expression should be read from left to right.

- **What does the expression $t < 9$ represent in this problem?** All bagels are less than 9 minutes old.

Try This!

- **A number can be a solution when it makes the statement $t < 9$ true. Why are 9 and 12 not solutions for this inequality?** These numbers are not less than 9.

- **What are possible whole-number solutions for $t < 9$?** Possible answers: 0, 1, 2, 3, 4, 5, 6, 7, 8

Use Math Talk to focus on students' understanding of inequality symbols.

PG76 Planning Guide

This lesson builds on comparisons presented in Chapter 3, and prepares students for inequalities in Grade 6.

Name _____
Understand Inequalities
Essential Question How can you use inequalities to solve problems?

Unlock the Problem

Every morning, Bobbi's Hot Bagels makes a special claim. All bagels Bobbi's sells will be warm and less than 9 minutes old. What **inequality** can you write to represent in whole minutes how old Bobbi's bagels are?

An inequality is a number sentence that compares two unequal quantities and uses the symbols $<$, $>$, $\leq$, or $\geq$.

- What clue words tell you that this problem involves an inequality?
  Possible answer: the words *less than*

🔒 **Write an inequality using a variable.**

STEP 1 Write the inequality in words.
time ⟶ is less than ⟶ 9

STEP 2 Replace *time* with the variable *t*.
t ⟶ less than ⟶ 9

STEP 3 Replace the words *less than* with a *less than* ($<$) symbol.
$t < 9$

Try This! Graph the solutions on the number line. Of 3, 6, 9, and 12, which numbers are solutions for $t < 9$?

STEP 1 In $t < 9$, replace t with 3.
Repeat the process for $t = 6, 9, 12$.
$t < 9$
$3 < 9$ ⟵ true

STEP 2 Identify the values that make $t < 9$ true.
True values are solutions: $t = 3, 6$.
False values are not solutions: $t \neq 9, 12$.
$6 < 9$ ⟵ true
$9 < 9$ ⟵ false
$12 < 9$ ⟵ false

STEP 3 Graph the solutions on a number line.
Graph true values with filled circles.

solutions

0 1 2 3 4 5 6 7 8 9 10 11 12 13 14

Possible answer: 9 would also be a solution for the inequality.

Math Talk **Mathematical Practices**
How does the answer for the problem change if the inequality is "*t* is less than or equal to 9"?

Getting Ready for Grade 6   GR31

GR: Practice, p. GRP14

Name _____
Understand Inequalities

ALGEBRA
Lesson 14

Of 2, 10, and 18, which numbers are solutions for the inequality?
1. $b < 15$ ___2, 10___
2. $d \geq 8$ ___10, 18___
3. $r \leq 18$ ___2, 10, 18___

Of 1, 3, 5, and 11, which numbers are solutions for the inequality?
4. $t < 2$ ___1___
5. $s > 0$ ___1, 3, 5, 11___
6. $g \geq 4$ ___5, 11___

Show two solutions for the inequality on a number line.

Possible answers are shown. Check students' number lines.

7. $c > 10$
1 2 3 4 5 6 7 8 9 10 11 12

8. $f \leq 3$
1 2 3 4 5 6 7 8 9 10 11 12

Problem Solving

9. A sign posted at a roller coaster states that all riders must be at least 48 inches tall in order to ride the coaster. Write an inequality using a variable that represents this situation.
Possible answer: $h \geq 48$, where h represents height

10. Ansley wants to drink at least 64 ounces of water per day, but not more than 72 ounces. How many ounces of water per day might she drink? Name all of the whole number possibilities.
Ansley might drink 64, 65, 66, 67, 68, 69, 70, 71, or 72 ounces of water per day.

GRP14

GR: Reteach, p. GRR14

Name _____

Lesson 14
Reteach

Algebra • Understand Inequalities

An **inequality** is a mathematical sentence that compares two quantities. An inequality contains an inequality symbol: $<$, $>$, $\leq$, $\geq$, or $\neq$.

Inequality Symbols

$<$ less than	$>$ greater than	$\leq$ less than or equal to	$\geq$ greater than or equal to	$\neq$ not equal to

The speed limit on a certain road is 45 miles per hour. A driver does not want to exceed the speed limit. Write an inequality using a variable to represent the driver's speed.

Step 1 Write the inequality in words.   speed is less than or equal to 45

Step 2 Replace speed with the variable s. s is less than or equal to 45

Step 3 Replace less than or equal to with $\leq$. $s \leq 45$

So, the inequality $s \leq 45$ represents a driver's speed if he doesn't want to exceed the speed limit of 45 miles per hour.

Of 4, 8, 12, and 16, which numbers are solutions for $t \geq 8$? Graph the solutions on a number line.

Step 1 In $t \geq 8$, replace t with 4. Repeat the process for $t = 8, 12, 16$. $t \geq 8$

Step 2 Identify the values that make $t \geq 8$ true.
True values are solutions: $t = 8, 12, 16$
False values are not solutions: $t \neq 4$

$4 \geq 8$ false
$8 \geq 8$ true
$12 \geq 8$ true
$16 \geq 8$ true

Step 3 Graph the solutions on a number line. Use filled circles.

0 1 2 3 4 5 6 7 8 9 10 11 12 13 14 15 16

Of 3, 5, and 8, which numbers are solutions for the inequality $k > 57$? Graph the solutions on the number line.
1. Replace k with 3. True or false?   false
2. Replace k with 5. True or false?   false
3. Replace k with 8. True or false?   true

0 1 2 3 4 5 6 7 8 9 10

Reteach
GRR14

Grade 5

*GR – Getting Ready Lessons and Resources (*www.thinkcentral.com*)

Share and Show

Of 2, 5, and 8, which numbers are solutions for the inequality $x \geq 5$?
Graph the solutions on the number line.

1a. Replace x with 2. True or false?

2 ≥ 5, false

1b. Replace x with 5. True or false?

5 ≥ 5, true

1c. Replace x with 8. True or false?

8 ≥ 5, true

Show two solutions for the inequality on a number line.

2. $a < 6$

Sample answers are shown.
Any value less than 6 is correct.

On Your Own

Of 7, 10, and 13, which numbers are solutions for the inequality?

3. $m > 8$
10, 13

4. $b \leq 10$
7, 10

5. $c < 15$
7, 10, 13

Of 0, 4, 6, and 11, which numbers are solutions for the inequality?

6. $d \geq 8$
11

7. $r < 1$
0

8. $s > 4$
6, 11

Show two solutions for the inequality on a number line.

9. $n \leq 6$

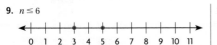

10. $x > 2$

Problem Solving

Possible answers are shown. Check students' number lines.

11. For her birthday party, Dina wants to invite at least 8 guests but not more than 12 guests. How many guests might she have? Name all of the possibilities.

Dina can have 8, 9, 10, 11, or 12 guests.

GR32

© Houghton Mifflin Harcourt Publishing Company

---

2 PRACTICE

▶ **Share and Show • Guided Practice**

Remind students to use the number line so that they can see a graphic representation of the solutions.

▶ **On Your Own • Independent Practice**

Students may choose to draw number lines for each response. For Exercises 4, 6, and 9, remind students of the meanings of these symbols.

▶ **Problem Solving** Common Core **MATHEMATICAL PRACTICES**

Encourage students to write an inequality that describes the correct responses.

3 SUMMARIZE

Common Core **MATHEMATICAL PRACTICES**

Essential Question

How can you use inequalities to solve problems? First, write an inequality using words. Then, replace key terms with variables. Use a number line to find the true solutions.

Math Journal WRITE ▸Math

Explain how you can decide which of 5, 7, and 9 are solutions of $k \geq 7$.

Getting Ready Lessons and Resources, pp. GR33–GR34 ✓**Checkpoint**

Name _____

✓ Checkpoint

Concepts and Skills

Write an integer to represent the situation.

1. a shark 125 feet below sea level ‾125

2. a bank deposit of 300 dollars ⁺300

Write an integer to represent the situation. Then, tell what it represents.

Situation	Integer	What Does 0 Represent?
3. a gain of 13 yards by a football team	⁺13	neither gaining nor losing yards
4. a temperature of 25 degrees below zero	‾25	a temperature of zero degrees

Write an expression. Then evaluate the expression for the value given.

5. Miki has n dollars. Dora has 3 more dollars than Miki. How many dollars does Dora have? Evaluate for $n = 14$.
$n + 3$; $17

6. Chip has s shells. Gina has 4 times as many shells as Chip. How many shells does Gina have? Evaluate for $s = 6$.
$4 \times s$; 24 shells

Of 1, 3, 4, and 8, which numbers are solutions for the inequality?

7. $a < 7$
1, 3, 4

8. $b \geq 3$
3, 4, 8

9. $c > 4$
8

10. $d \leq 8$
1, 3, 4, 8

Problem Solving

Filters are set up to sort pennies, dimes, and nickels. A penny is 19 mm wide, a dime is 17.9 mm wide, and a nickel is 21 mm wide. Coins less than 20 mm wide will pass through the first level, and coins less than 18.5 mm wide will pass through the second level.

drop coins
Level 1   20 mm
Level 2   18.5 mm

11. If you drop a large number of 3 coins from above, which coins will be caught at Level 1? Which coins will pass through?
nickels; Dimes and pennies pass.

12. Which coins will be caught at Level 2? Which coins will pass through?
pennies; Dimes pass.

Fill in the bubble completely to show your answer.

13. The lowest temperature ever recorded in North Dakota was 60 degrees below zero Fahrenheit. Which integer represents the temperature?
Ⓐ 0
Ⓑ 60
Ⓒ ‾60
Ⓓ ‾0

14. In football, a team receives 3 points for each field goal it makes. Which expression shows the number of points a team will receive for making f field goals?
Ⓐ 3 + f
Ⓑ 3 × f
Ⓒ f − 3
Ⓓ f ÷ 3

15. The elevation of Central City is 84 feet above sea level. Which integer is the opposite of 84?
Ⓐ 48
Ⓑ ‾84
Ⓒ ‾48
Ⓓ 84

16. Uncle Louie is at least 1 inch shorter than Miriam, and at least 2 inches taller than Jeffrey. Jeffrey's height is 64 inches. Miriam is not more than 5 inches taller than Jeffrey. Which answer choice could be Uncle Louie's height?
Ⓐ 65 inches
Ⓑ 67 inches
Ⓒ 69 inches
Ⓓ 70 inches

Getting Ready for Grade 6   GR33   GR34

© Houghton Mifflin Harcourt Publishing Company

LESSON 15

Polygons on a Coordinate Grid

LESSON AT A GLANCE

Common Core Standards
Graph points on the coordinate plane to solve real-world and mathematical problems.
5.G.A.1 Use a pair of perpendicular number lines, called axes, to define a coordinate system, with the intersection of the lines (the origin) arranged to coincide with the 0 on each line and a given point in the plane located by using an ordered pair of numbers, called its coordinates. Understand that the first number indicates how far to travel from the origin in the direction of one axis, and the second number indicates how far to travel in the direction of the second axis, with the convention that the names of the two axes and the coordinates correspond (e.g., *x*-axis and

x-coordinate, *y*-axis and *y*-coordinate).

Solve real-world and mathematical problems involving area, surface area, and volume.
6.G.A.3 Draw polygons in the coordinate plane given coordinates for the vertices; use coordinates to find the length of a side joining points with the same first coordinate or the same second coordinate. Apply these techniques in the context of solving real-world and mathematical problems.

Lesson Objective
Plot polygons on a coordinate grid.

Materials
MathBoard

1 TEACH and TALK

▶ **Unlock the Problem**

(Common Core) **MATHEMATICAL PRACTICES**

Have students read the problem.

- **How do you decide where to plot the point (10, 1)?** I start at (0, 0). I go right 10 units, and then up 1 unit.

- **Are the points (6, 10) and (10, 6) the same points? Explain.** No. Possible explanation: (6, 10) is 6 units to the right of (0, 0) and 10 units up. (10, 6) is 10 units to the right of (0, 0) and 6 units up.

- **What if the two vertices (2, 1) and (2, 6) were replaced by a single vertex at (6, 1). What would the shape of the floor be?** a trapezoid

- **(0, 0) is the vertex of the right angle of a right triangle plotted on a coordinate grid. Give two points that could form the other two vertices.** Possible answer: (4, 0) and (0, 4) Students' answers should include a point on the *x*-axis and a point on the *y*-axis.

Use **Math Talk** to focus on students' understanding of lesson concepts.

PG78 Planning Guide

This lesson builds on graphing in quadrant I of the coordinate plane presented in Chapter 9, and prepares students to graph points for the vertices of a polygon in the coordinate plane taught in Grade 6.

Name _____

Polygons on a Coordinate Grid

Essential Question How can you plot polygons on a coordinate grid?

Connect You have learned to plot points on a coordinate grid. You can use that skill to plot polygons on a coordinate grid.

 Unlock the Problem Real World

Camille is designing an indoor greenhouse on a coordinate grid. The floor of the greenhouse is a polygon. The vertices of the polygon can be graphed using the coordinates shown in the table. Plot and describe the floor of the greenhouse.

x	y
10	1
2	6
2	1
6	10
10	6

- **What do *x* and *y* represent in the table?** Each (x, y) pair represents the x- and y-coordinates of a point.

🔒 Plot the polygon on a coordinate grid.

STEP 1 Write ordered pairs.

Use each row of the table to write an ordered pair.

(10, 1), (2, **6**), (**2** , **1**),
(**6** , **10**), (**10** , **6**).

STEP 2 Graph a point for each pair on the coordinate grid.

STEP 3 Connect the points.

So, the floor of the greenhouse is a **pentagon** .

- **What if** the greenhouse floor had only four of the five vertices given in the table and did not include (6, 10). What would the shape of the floor be? **a rectangle**

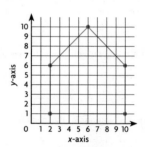

- A parallelogram on a coordinate grid has vertices at (3, 4), (6, 1), and (8, 4). What are the coordinates of the fourth vertex? **Explain** how you found the answer.
(1, 1), (5, 7), or (11, 1); Possible answer: I plotted the three points on a coordinate grid and joined them to make three sides of a parallelogram. I used the shape to find the fourth vertex.

Possible answer: The number of sides equal the number of vertices.

 Math Talk **Mathematical Practices**

Suppose you know the vertices of a polygon. How can you identify what type of polygon it is without plotting the vertices on a coordinate grid?

Getting Ready for Grade 6 GR35

GR: Practice, p. GRP15

Name _____ **Lesson 15**
Polygons on a Coordinate Grid

Plot the polygon with the given vertices on a coordinate grid. Identify the polygon.

1. (1, 9), (3, 2), (7, 2), (9, 9), (5, 10)

pentagon

2. (1, 6), (6, 1), (8, 9)

triangle

3. (1, 9), (2, 1), (9, 1), (8, 9)

parallelogram

4. (2, 3), (5, 1), (8, 3), (8, 7), (5, 9), (2, 7)

hexagon

Problem Solving Real World

5. A square tile measures 12 inches by 12 inches. Each unit on a coordinate grid represents 1 inch. (1, 1) and (1, 13) are two of the vertices of the tile drawn on the grid. What are the coordinates of the other two vertices?
(13, 1), (13, 13)

GRP15

GR: Reteach, p. GRR15

Name _____ **Lesson 15**
Reteach
Polygons on a Coordinate Grid

Isabella is designing a quilt on a coordinate grid. The quilt is made up of polygons sewn together. The vertices of one of the polygons can be graphed using the coordinates shown in the table. Plot and describe the polygon.

Plot the points on a coordinate grid.

Step 1 Write ordered pairs.

Use each row of the table to write an ordered pair.

(1, 9), (3, 3), (7, 3), (8, 9), (7, 9), (5, 9)

Step 2 Graph a point for each pair on the coordinate grid.

Step 3 Connect the points.

So, the polygon has the shape of a **hexagon** .

Plot the polygon with the given vertices on a coordinate grid. Identify the polygon.

1. (1, 4), (8, 1), (6, 9)

triangle

2. (1, 1), (1, 5), (9, 5), (9, 1)

rectangle

Reteach GRR15 Grade 5

---

*GR – Getting Ready Lessons and Resources (*www.thinkcentral.com*)

Share and Show

Plot the polygon with the given vertices on a coordinate grid.
Identify the polygon.

1. (9, 6), (1, 7), (3, 1)

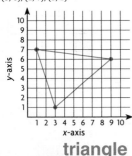

__triangle__

2. (1, 6), (8, 4), (1, 4), (8, 6)

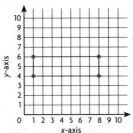

__rectangle__

On Your Own

Plot the polygon with the given vertices on a coordinate grid.
Identify the polygon.

3. (2, 10), (10, 2), (10, 10), (2, 2)

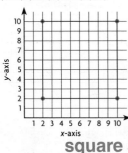

__square__

4. (10, 4), (2, 10), (3, 1), (8, 0), (7, 10), (1, 7)

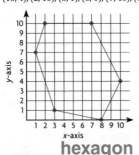

__hexagon__

Problem Solving

5. A football field is a rectangle measuring 300 ft by 160 ft. Each unit on a
coordinate grid represents 1 foot. (0, 0) and (0, 160) are two of the coordinates of
a football field drawn on the grid. What are the coordinates
of the other two vertices?

(300, 0) and (300, 160)

GR36

© Houghton Mifflin Harcourt Publishing Company

PRACTICE

▶ **Share and Show • Guided Practice**

Some students may need to be reminded
that the first number of a coordinate pair is
the *x*-coordinate and the second number is
the *y*-coordinate.

▶ **On Your Own • Independent Practice**

For Exercise 4, be sure students understand
that they should plot the point (8, 0) on the
x-axis.

▶ **Problem Solving**  MATHEMATICAL PRACTICES

You may wish to suggest that students draw
the football field on a coordinate grid where
each unit represents 20 feet.

3 SUMMARIZE

Common Core MATHEMATICAL PRACTICES

Essential Question

**How can you plot polygons on a coordinate
grid?** Possible answer: write the ordered pairs representing the vertices of the polygon. Graph a point for each pair
on the coordinate grid. Then connect the points to form the
polygon.

Math Journal ▌WRITE ▶ *Math*

**Draw a triangle on a coordinate grid. Write
the ordered pairs that represent the vertices
of the triangle and explain how you found
each ordered pair on the coordinate grid.**

LESSON 16

Area of a Parallelogram

LESSON AT A GLANCE

Common Core Standards

Solve problems involving measurement and conversion of measurements from a larger unit to a smaller unit.
4.MD.A.3 Apply the area and perimeter formulas for rectangles in real world and mathematical problems.

Solve real-world and mathematical problems involving area, surface area, and volume.
6.G.A.1 Find the area of right triangles, other triangles, special quadrilaterals, and polygons by composing into rectangles or decomposing into triangles and other shapes; apply these techniques in the context of solving real-world and mathematical problems.

Lesson Objective
Find the area of parallelograms.

Materials
MathBoard, grid paper (see *eTeacher Resources*), scissors

 GO DIGITAL Animated Math Models

1 TEACH and TALK GO DIGITAL • Animated Math Models

▶ **Activity**

Common Core **MATHEMATICAL PRACTICES**

Have students read the activity.

- **Describe how you will draw the parallelogram.** Possible answer: I will draw the lower base of the parallelogram, making it 12 units long. From the left end of the base I will count 3 units right and then 5 units up and mark a point. From that point I will draw the upper base of the parallelogram, making it 12 units long. Finally, I will connect the endpoints of the bases to make the sides of the parallelogram.

- **A student found the height of the rectangle by measuring the length of the slanting left side of the parallelogram. Was the student right? Explain.** No. Possible explanation: The height of the rectangle is the length of a line drawn perpendicular to the base, not on a slant from the base.

- **If you know the base and height of a parallelogram, do you have to draw it on grid paper, cut off one end, and make a rectangle in order to find its area? Explain.** No. I can find the area by multiplying the base times the height.

Use **Math Talk** to help students recognize that the area of a parallelogram can be found by multiplying the base times the height.

PG80 Planning Guide

This lesson builds on finding area of rectangles in Grade 4, and prepares students for finding the area of a parallelogram taught in Grade 6.

Name _____

Area of a Parallelogram

Essential Question How can you find the area of a parallelogram?

Connect You have learned that the area of a rectangle with base *b* and height *h* is $A = b \times h$. The rectangle shown has a base of 5 units and a height of 3 units. So, its area is $A = 5 \times 3 = 15$ square units. You can use what you have learned about the area of a rectangle to find the area of a parallelogram.

🔑 **Unlock the Problem** (Real World)

The souvenir stand at Mighty Grasshopper basketball games sells parallelogram-shaped pennants. Each pennant has a base of 12 inches and a height of 5 inches.

🔓 **Activity** Find the area of the parallelogram.

Materials ■ grid paper ■ scissors

STEP 1 Draw the parallelogram on grid paper and cut it out.

STEP 2 Cut along the dashed line to remove a right triangle.

STEP 3 Move the right triangle to the right side of the parallelogram to form a rectangle.

STEP 4 The base of the rectangle measures ___12___ inches.

The height of the rectangle measures ___5___ inches.

The area of the rectangle is
$12 \times$ ___5___ $=$ ___60___ square inches.

- **Explain** why the area of the parallelogram must equal the area of the rectangle.
Possible explanation: Both figures are made from the same amount of paper.

So, the area of a pennant is
___12___ $\times$ ___5___ $=$ ___60___ square inches.

Possible explanation: Multiply the base times the height.

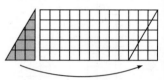

Math Talk | **Mathematical Practices**
Explain how to find the area of a parallelogram if you know the base and the height of the figure.

© Houghton Mifflin Harcourt Publishing Company

Getting Ready for Grade 6   GR37

GR: Practice, p. GRP16

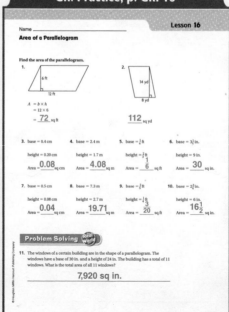

GR: Reteach, p. GRR16

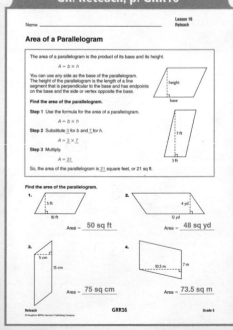

*GR – Getting Ready Lessons and Resources (*www.thinkcentral.com*)

Share and Show

Find the area of the parallelogram.

1. $A = b \times h$

$A = 8 \times 4$

$A = \underline{32}$ sq cm

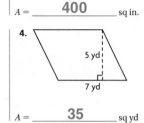
4 cm
8 cm

2.

20 in.
20 in.

$A = \underline{400}$ sq in.

3.
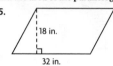
13 m
9 m

$A = \underline{117}$ sq m

4.
5 yd
7 yd

$A = \underline{35}$ sq yd

On Your Own

Find the area of the parallelogram.

5.
18 in.
32 in.

$A = \underline{576}$ sq in.

6.
2.5 cm
11.3 cm

$A = \underline{28.25}$ sq cm

7. base = 0.6 cm

height = 0.15 cm

$A = \underline{0.09}$ sq cm

8. base = 1.8 m

height = 2.9 m

$A = \underline{5.22}$ sq m

9. base = $\frac{1}{2}$ ft

height = $\frac{3}{8}$ ft

$A = \underline{\frac{3}{16}}$ sq ft

10. base = $4\frac{1}{4}$ in.

height = 20 in.

$A = \underline{85}$ sq in.

Problem Solving (Real World)

11. Carla made a border for her garden using parallelogram-shaped tiles. Each piece had a base of 4 in. and a height of $2\frac{1}{2}$ in. She used 85 tiles. What was the total area of the border?

$\underline{850 \text{ sq in.}}$

GR38

© Houghton Mifflin Harcourt Publishing Company

---

② PRACTICE

▶ **Share and Show • Guided Practice**

For Exercise 3, you may wish to point out that the base of a parallelogram does not have to be longer than the height. Remind students that they can find the area of a parallelogram by multiplying the base and height, as long as they know the length of one side and the height drawn perpendicular to that side.

▶ **On Your Own • Independent Practice**

Use Exercises 7–10 as a check on students' skills of finding the product of two decimals, two fractions, and a mixed number and a whole number.

▶ **Problem Solving** (Common Core) **MATHEMATICAL PRACTICES**

Exercise 11 is a multi-step problem. Students must first find the area of a single tile (4 in. × $2\frac{1}{2}$ in. = 10 in.²). Then, because there are 85 tiles, they should multiply the product by 85 (10 in.² × 85 = 850 in.²).

③ SUMMARIZE

(Common Core) **MATHEMATICAL PRACTICES**

Essential Question

How can you find the area of a parallelogram?

I can multiply the base times the height.

Math Journal WRITE ▸Math

Ronnie drew a parallelogram on grid paper. She cut off one end of the parallelogram and moved it to the other side to form a rectangle. Explain why the areas of the rectangle and the parallelogram were equal.

LESSON 17

Median and Mode

LESSON AT A GLANCE

Common Core Standards
Represent and interpret data.
5.MD.B.2 Make a line plot to display a data set of measurements in fractions of a unit (1/2, 1/4, 1/8). Use operations on fractions for this grade to solve problems involving information presented in line plots.

Summarize and describe distributions.
6.SP.B.5c Summarize numerical data sets in relation to their context, such as by: Giving quantitative measures of

center (median and/or mean) and variability (interquartile range and/or mean absolute deviation), as well as describing any overall pattern and any striking deviations from the overall pattern with reference to the context in which the data were gathered.

Lesson Objective
Summarize a data set by using median and mode.

Materials
MathBoard

 Animated Math Models

---

1 TEACH and TALK 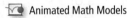 Animated Math Models

▶ **Unlock the Problem**

MATHEMATICAL PRACTICES

Discuss the new vocabulary.

- **Blake said that the median of the data set 3, 8, 2 is 8 because 8 is the middle value. Was he right? Explain.** No. Possible explanation: He didn't write the data in order before looking for the middle value. Written in order, the data set is 2, 3, 8. The median is the middle value, 3.

- **What is the median of the data set 1, 3, 5, 7? Why?** 4; Possible answer: There is an even number of values in the data set, so the median is the sum of the two middle items divided by 2; $(3 + 5) \div 2 = 8 \div 2 = 4$.

- **Give an example of a data set with no mode.** Possible answer: no mode: 5, 6, 7, 8

- **Estimate the mode of the data set consisting of the ages of all the students in the classroom.** Answers will vary. Students should estimate what they believe to be the most common age of the set of their classmates' ages.

PG82 Planning Guide

This lesson builds on analyzing data using operations presented in Chapter 9, and prepares students for describing quantitative measures in data taught in Grade 6.

Name _____

Median and Mode

Essential Question How can you describe a set of data using median and mode?

The **median** of a set of data is the middle value when the data are written in order. For example, a baseball team scored 6, 2, 6, 0, and 3 runs in five games. The median is 3 runs: 0, 2, ③, 6, 6.

If there is an even number of data items, the median is the sum of the two middle items divided by 2.

The **mode** of a data set is the data value or values that occur most often. A data set may have no mode, one mode, or several modes. The mode of the data set of baseball runs is 6.

Unlock the Problem

For the Science Fair, Ronni grew 9 sweet pea plants under different conditions. Here are the plants' heights, in centimeters: 11, 13, 6, 9, 15, 7, 9, 17, 12.

What are the median and mode of the data?

🔑 **Find the median and mode.**

STEP 1 Order the heights from least to greatest.

6, 7, __9__, __9__, ⑪, __12__, __13__, __15__, __17__

STEP 2 Circle the middle value.

So, the median is __11__ centimeters.

STEP 3 Identify the data value that occurs most often. __9__ occurs two times.

So, the mode is __9__ centimeters.

- How can you find the median if there is an even number of data items?
  Divide the sum of the two middle items by 2.

Math Talk **Mathematical Practices**
Give an example of a data set with two modes.

Possible answer: 5, 6, 6, 6, 7, 8, 8, 8

Try This! Find the median and mode of the numbers: 8, 11, 13, 6, 4, 3.

STEP 1 Order the numbers from least to greatest.

__3__, __4__, __6__, __8__, __11__, 13

STEP 2 There is an even number of data items, so divide the sum of the two middle items by 2. $\frac{6 + 8}{2} = \frac{14}{2} = 7$

So, the median is = __7__.

STEP 3 __No__ data value appears more than once.

So, the data set has __no__ mode.

Getting Ready for Grade 6   GR39

GR: Practice, p. GRP17

Name _____   Lesson 17
Median and Mode

Find the median and the mode of the data.

1. daily low temperatures the first 7 days of February (°F): 25, 24, 25, 27, 25, 15
median: __25 °F__
mode: __25 °F__

2. lengths of 8 songs played on the radio (minutes): 2, 3, 3, 5, 4, 3, 4, 3
median: __3 minutes__
mode: __3 minutes__

3. ages of 9 children at a dentist's office: 9, 10, 10, 8, 7, 9, 5, 12, 10
median: __9 yrs__
mode: __10 yrs__

4. number of touchdowns scored per game: 1, 0, 3, 4, 2, 2, 3, 4, 1, 3
median: __2.5 touchdowns__
mode: __3 touchdowns__

5. number of exercises on math homework for one week: 12, 25, 15, 18, 13
median: __15 exercises__
mode: __none__

6. number of tacos eaten per person: 2, 3, 3, 4, 4, 2, 5, 1, 3, 1
median: __3 tacos__
mode: __3, 4 tacos__

7. amount earned per hour for babysitting ($): 10, 10, 6, 9, 12
median: $ __9.50__
mode: $ __10__

8. number of days per month: 31, 28, 31, 30, 31, 30, 31, 31, 30, 31, 30, 31
median: __31 days__
mode: __31 days__

Problem Solving

9. Jasmine surveys her classmates and records the number of siblings each person has. What are the median and mode of her data?
median: __2 siblings__
mode: __1__

Number of Siblings Per Classmate
2—0—2—2—3—1—4—2—2—5
4—1—0—1—1—2—1—3—1—1

GRP17

GR: Reteach, p. GRR17

Name _____   Lesson 17
Reteach
Median and Mode

The **median** of a set of data is the middle value when the data are written in order.

0, 3, 7, 8, 11
median

If a set of data contains an even number of items, the median is the sum of the two middle terms divided by 2.

The **mode** of a set of data is the data value or values that occur most often. A set of data may have no mode, one mode, or more than one mode.

0, 1, 4, 2, 13, 1

In the data set above, 1 is the mode because it occurs the most often.

The list shows the numbers of books 12 students read during summer vacation.

2, 3, 4, 1, 4, 5, 3, 6, 2, 4, 3, 4

What are the median and mode of the data?

Step 1 Order the numbers from least to greatest.

1, 2, 2, 3, 3, ③, ④, 4, 4, 4, 5, 6

Step 2 To find the median, circle the middle values. Since there are 12 values, circle the two middle values. Find the sum of the two middle values and divide by 2.

$3 + 4 = 7$ $7 \div 2 = 3.5$

So, the median is 3.5 books.

Step 3 To find the mode, identify the data value that occurs most often. 4 occurs 4 times. So, the mode is 4 books.

Find the median and mode of the data.

1. number of minutes to run 1 mi: 7, 9, 8, 9, 7, 9, 8
median: __8 mins__
mode: __9 mins__

2. Callie's quiz scores: 95, 87, 93, 100, 87, 95
median: __94__
mode: __87, 95__

Reteach   GRR17   Grade 5

---

*GR – Getting Ready Lessons and Resources (*www.thinkcentral.com*)

Share and Show

Find the median and the mode of the data.

1. puppies' weights (pounds): 8, 3, 5, 3, 2, 6, 3

   Order the weights: **2, 3, 3, 3, 5, 6, 8**

   The median, or middle value, is **3** pounds

   The mode, or most common value,
   is **3** pounds.

2. numbers of students in math classes:
   25, 21, 22, 18, 23, 24, 25

   median: **23** students

   mode: **25** students

3. numbers of 3-point baskets made:
   2, 0, 5, 4, 5, 2, 5, 2

   median: **3** 3-point baskets

   mode: **2, 5** 3-point baskets

4. movie ticket prices ($):
   8, 8, 6, 8, 7, 6, 8, 10, 8, 6

   median: $ **8**

   mode: $ **8**

On Your Own

Find the median and the mode of the data.

5. ages of first 10 U.S. presidents
   when inaugurated:
   57, 61, 57, 57, 58, 57, 61, 54, 68, 51

   median: **57** years

   mode: **57** years

6. weights of rock samples (pounds):
   39, 28, 21, 47, 40, 33

   median: **36** pounds

   mode: **none** pounds

7. lengths of humpback whale songs (minutes): 25,
   29, 31, 22, 33, 31, 26, 22

   median: **27.5** minutes

   mode: **22, 31** minutes

8. Sascha's test scores:
   90, 88, 79, 97, 100, 97, 92, 88, 85, 92

   median: **91**

   mode: **88, 92, 97**

Problem Solving (Real World)

9. Adrian recorded the daily high temperatures the first two weeks of July.
   What were the median and mode of her data?

   median: **99.5** °F

   mode: **98** °F

Daily High Temperatures (°F)						
101	99	98	96	102	101	98
101	98	95	100	102	98	102

© Houghton Mifflin Harcourt Publishing Company

GR40

② PRACTICE

▶ **Share and Show • Guided Practice**

Encourage students to check each ordered set of data that they write to be sure that they have included every item from the original data set in their ordered set exactly once.

▶ **On Your Own • Independent Practice**

The data sets in Exercises 5–8 all have even numbers of items. To find the median of any set whose middle two items are different, students should divide the sum of the two items by 2.

▶ **Problem Solving** Common Core **MATHEMATICAL PRACTICES**

Ask students how they could change one temperature so that there would be two modes. Possible changes: change 95 to 101 or 102.

③ SUMMARIZE

Common Core **MATHEMATICAL PRACTICES**

Essential Question

How can you describe a set of data using median and mode? Possible answer: In a set of data, the median is the middle value when all values are placed in order. If there is an even number of values, the two middle values are added and divided by 2. The mode is the value or values that occurs most often.

Math Journal WRITE ▸ Math

Explain how to find the median and mode of the data set {3, 7, 6, 1, 7}.

LESSON 18

Finding the Average

LESSON AT A GLANCE

Common Core Standards

Represent and interpret data.

5.MD.B.2 Make a line plot to display a data set of measurements in fractions of a unit (1/2, 1/4, 1/8). Use operations on fractions for this grade to solve problems involving information presented in line plots.

Summarize and describe distributions.

6.SP.B.5c Summarize numerical data sets in relation to their context, such as by: Giving quantitative measures of center (median and/or mean) and variability (interquartile range and/or mean absolute deviation), as well as describing any overall pattern and any striking deviations from the overall pattern with reference to the context in which the data were gathered.

Lesson Objective
Find the average of a group of values.

Materials
calculators, MathBoard

GO DIGITAL 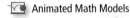 Animated Math Models

---

1 TEACH and TALK **GO DIGITAL** • Animated Math Models

▶ Unlock the Problem

MATHEMATICAL PRACTICES

Help students understand how to use division to find the average of a group of numbers.

Distribute calculators to pairs of students, and review basic operations with the calculator.

Discuss the meaning of the term *average*. Clarify with students that an average is the number that can be considered to be typical of a set of numbers.

Have students look at the list of numbers in the table on GR41, and ask them to predict the average.

- **Add the numbers in the column. What is the sum?** 170

- **How many numbers are there?** 5 **What is the quotient when you divide 170 by 5?** 34 **So 34 is the average of this group of numbers.**

Use Math Talk to focus on students' understanding of lesson concepts.

Name _____

Finding the Average

Essential Question How can you find the average of a set of values?

An average of a set of data can be found by finding the sum of the group of numbers from the data and then dividing by the number of addends.

For example, if Anne scores 21 points, 22 points, and 17 points in 3 different basketball games, she scores an average of 20 points per game. This is because 21 + 22 + 17 = 60, and 60 ÷ 3, the total number of points divided by the number of games, is 20.

> This lesson builds on analyzing data presented in Chapter 9, and prepares students for describing quantitative measures in data taught in Grade 6.

 Unlock the Problem Real World

Jonathon and Pilar are practicing to be a juggling team. The table shows the number of seconds they were able to keep 4 balls in the air without making a mistake. What was the average number of seconds they were able to juggle?

Trial	Seconds
a	32
b	8
c	62
d	55
e	13

- **How many trials did they record?**
  5

Find the average of the times.

STEP 1 Find the sum of the seconds.   32 + 8 + 62 + 55 + 13 = 170

STEP 2 How many numbers did you add?   5 numbers

STEP 3 Divide the sum by the number of addends. $5)\overline{170}$ = 34

So, the average time that Jonathon and Pilar kept 4 balls in the air was **34** seconds per trial.

Try This! Find the average of 61, 99, 106, 3, 44, and 89.

STEP 1 Find the sum.

61 + 99 + 106 + 3 + 44 + 89 = **402**

STEP 2 Divide the sum by the number of addends.

402 ÷ 6 = **67**

So, the average of 61, 99, 106, 3, 44, and 89 is **67**.

Possible answer: They might juggle for about 34 seconds before they make a mistake.

Math Talk Mathematical Practices

Use the jugglers' average time per trial. What might you expect of them in their next trial?

© Houghton Mifflin Harcourt Publishing Company

Getting Ready for Grade 6   GR41

GR: Practice, p. GRP18

Name _____   Lesson 18

Finding the Average

Find the average of the set of numbers.

1. 1, 3, 9, 7
   1 + 3 + 9 + 7 = 20
   20 ÷ 4 = 5
   5

2. 10, 18, 20, 8, 11, 17   **14**

3. 100, 120, 105, 115, 110   **110**

4. 18, 28, 50, 92, 116, 74   **63**

5. 737, 843, 188, 592   **590**

6. 8, 11, 16, 7, 25, 9, 3, 8, 12   **11**

7. 2,639; 1,001; 1,708; 200   **1,387**

8. 24, 23, 22, 24, 26, 24, 30, 33, 34, 30   **27**

9. 70, 53, 43, 91, 0, 104, 68, 24, 51   **56**

10. 16, 32, 48, 56, 60, 76   **48**

11. 10, 9, 8, 10, 12, 11, 16, 19, 10, 15   **12**

12. 270, 261, 251, 299, 208, 312, 276, 232, 259   **264**

13. Find the average amount of snowfall.

Month	1	2	3	4	5	6	7
Amount of Snowfall (in.)	44	28	23	15	2	0	0

16 in.

Problem Solving Real World

14. In the snowfall table above, suppose the amount of snowfall for each of the next three months was 6 inches. By how much would this change the average amount of snowfall over the entire period?

3 in.

GRP18

GR: Reteach, p. GRR18

Nome _____   Lesson 18
Reteach

Finding the Average

An **average** of a set of data is the sum of the data values divided by the total number of data values.

For example, suppose you have the data set 4, 0, 24, 28, and 14. The sum of the data values is 4 + 0 + 24 + 28 + 14, or 70. There are a total of 5 data values. So the average is 70 ÷ 5, or 14.

Several friends are participating in a walk-a-thon for charity. The table at the right shows the amount of money each friend raised. What is the average amount of money raised by each friend?

Name	Amount of Money Raised ($)
Aki	85
Stephen	90
Lainie	100
Janelle	75
Azumi	115

Step 1 Find the total amount of money the friends raised.

85 + 90 + 100 + 75 + 115 = 465

Step 2 Determine how many friends raised money for the walk-a-thon.

Aki	Stephen	Lainie	Janelle	Azumi
1	2	3	4	5

A total of 5 friends raised money.

Step 3 Divide the total amount of money, 465, by the total number of friends, 5, who raised the money.

465 ÷ 5 = 93

So, the average amount of money raised by each friend is $93.

Ana Lisa's runs batted in (RBI) record is shown for this month. What was the average number of runs that Ana Lisa batted in per game?

Game	1	2	3	4	5	6	7	8	9	10
Number of RBIs	3	4	1	2	2	2	3	1	2	

1. Find the total number of runs Ana Lisa batted in.   **20 runs**

2. In how many games did Ana Lisa play?   **10 games**

3. Divide the sum by the number of games. What is the average number of runs batted in per game?   **2 runs**

Find the average of the set of numbers.

4. 16, 22, 19, 14, 24   **19**

5. 40, 36, 51, 36, 29, 18   **35**

Reteach   GRR18   Grade 5

***GR** – Getting Ready Lessons and Resources (www.thinkcentral.com)*

Share and Show

Tommy's basketball scoring record is shown for this month. What was the average number of points that Tommy scored per game?

1a. Find the sum of the points Tommy scored.

136 points

Game	1	2	3	4	5	6	7	8
Points	24	11	31	14	9	21	18	8

1b. How many numbers did you add to find the sum in Exercise 1?

8

1c. Divide the sum by the number of games. What is the average number of points per game?

17 points

Find the average of the set of numbers.

2. 6, 9, 14, 4, 12

9

3. 44, 55, 33, 22, 40, 40

39

On Your Own

Find the average of the set of numbers.

4. 4, 8, 12, 14, 15, 19

12

5. 28, 20, 31, 17

24

6. 100, 140, 60, 120, 180

120

7. 17, 91, 49, 73, 115, 27

62

8. 5, 8, 13, 4, 22, 6, 0, 5, 9

8

9. 637, 492, 88, 743

490

10. 2,439; 801; 1,508; 0

1,187

11. 13, 12, 11, 13, 15, 13, 19, 22, 13, 19

15

12. 78, 61, 51, 99, 8, 112, 76, 32, 59

64

13. Find the average temperature.

52°F

Day	1	2	3	4	5	6	7
Temperature (°F)	48	59	38	53	61	61	44

Problem Solving

14. In the temperature table above, suppose the temperature for the next 2 days was 70 degrees. By how much would this change the average temperature over the entire period?

4 degrees

GR42

2 PRACTICE

▶ Share and Show • Guided Practice

Remind students to check their average to see if it makes sense: **Does the average number look "typical" of that group of numbers?**

▶ On Your Own • Independent Practice

Encourage students to practice addition and division skills by completing problems with paper and pencil and estimating to check.

▶ Problem Solving   Common Core MATHEMATICAL PRACTICES

Help students break the problem into steps by first calculating the average of the existing group of numbers, and then calculating a new average by including 70 and 70.

3 SUMMARIZE

Common Core MATHEMATICAL PRACTICES

Essential Question

How can you find the average of a set of values? Find the sum of the numbers. Count how many numbers are in the set. Divide the sum by the number of addends.

Math Journal   WRITE ▶ Math

The ages of the five members of the Garcia family are 6, 41, 9, 11, and 43. What is the average age of the family members? Explain how you found the answer.

Histograms

LESSON AT A GLANCE

Common Core Standards
Represent and interpret data.
3.MD.B.3 Draw a scaled picture graph and a scaled bar graph to represent a data set with several categories. Solve one- and two-step "how many more" and "how many less" problems using information presented in scaled bar graphs.

Summarize and describe distributions.
6.SP.B.4 Display numerical data in plots on a number line, including dot plots, histograms, and box plots.

Lesson Objective
Make a histogram to organize data.

Vocabulary
histogram

Materials
MathBoard

GO DIGITAL ☑ Animated Math Models

---

1 TEACH and TALK GO DIGITAL · Animated Math Models

▶ **Activity** Common Core **MATHEMATICAL PRACTICES**

Have students read the Activity.

- **What are the ages of the youngest and oldest members of the bicycle club?** 17; 59

- **How does knowing the ages of the youngest and oldest members help you organize the data?** Possible answer: It helps in choosing reasonable intervals for the frequency table.

- **How does knowing the number of members in each age interval help you make the histogram?** Possible answer: It helps to choose an appropriate scale and interval for the vertical axis of the histogram.

- **How can you check that you have included each member of the bicycle club in the histogram?** Possible answer: The sum of the values represented by the bars should be 28 since there are 28 members in the bicycle club.

Use **Math Talk** to check students' understanding of how a histogram and bar graph are different.

PG86 Planning Guide

This lesson builds on bar graphs presented in Grade 3, and prepares students for displaying data in a histogram taught in Grade 6.

Name _____

Histograms

Essential Question How can you use a histogram to organize data?

🔑 Unlock the Problem *Real World*

🔑 **Activity** The table below shows the ages of the members of a bicycle club. Make a **histogram** of the data. A histogram is a bar graph that shows how often data occur in intervals.

Math Idea
In a histogram, the bars touch because they represent continuous intervals.

Ages of Members in a Bicycle Club									
34	38	29	41	40	35	50	20	47	22	19	21	18	17
26	30	41	43	52	45	28	25	39	24	23	25	50	59

STEP 1 Make a frequency table with intervals of 10. Fill in the frequencies.

STEP 2 Choose an appropriate scale and interval for the vertical axis, and list the intervals on the horizontal axis. Label each axis.

STEP 3 Draw a bar for each interval. Give the histogram a title.

Ages	Tally	Frequency
10–19	III	3
20–29	IIII IIII	10
30–39	IIII	5
40–49	IIIII	6
50–59	IIII	4

Ages of Members in a Bicycle Club

- **What if** you changed the histogram to show four age groups with 12-year intervals?

How would the histogram change?

Possible answer: There would only be 4 bars but the frequencies would still add up to the same number. Each interval would include more ages.
Possible explanation: In a bar graph with categories, there are spaces between the bars. A histogram shows frequencies, and there is no space between the bars.

Math Talk **Mathematical Practices**
Explain how a histogram and a bar graph with categories are different.

Getting Ready for Grade 6 **GR43**

GR: Practice, p. GRP19

Name _____ Lesson 19
Histograms

For 1–3, use the histogram at the right.
The amount of time, in minutes, that it takes students in Lacey's class to get to school by bus is shown below.

10, 25, 12, 20, 15, 6, 27, 13, 22, 30, 19, 9, 11, 17, 26, 21, 18, 20, 28, 16

Time on Bus

1. Use 10-minute intervals starting at 0. List the intervals.
   0–9, 10–19, 20–29, 30–39

2. Make a frequency table of the data.
   Check students' frequency tables.

3. Complete the histogram of the data.
   Check students' histograms.

For 4–6, use the data below to make a histogram.
The heights, in inches, of the saplings in the nursery are shown below.

60, 48, 52, 64, 56, 59, 63, 58, 62, 65, 50, 57, 49, 60, 61, 67, 55, 58, 62, 63, 59, 56, 64, 65, 54, 51, 62, 57, 58, 64

4. Use 10-inch intervals for the data. List the intervals.
   Possible answer: 40–49, 50–59, 60–69

5. Make a frequency table of the data.
   Check students' frequency tables.

6. Make a histogram of the data.
   Check students' histograms.

Problem Solving *Real World*

7. Use a smaller interval for the heights in Exercises 4–6. List the intervals. **Possible answer: 45–49, 50–54, 55–59, 60–64, 65–69**

8. How does the histogram change? **Possible answer: The tallest bar is shorter than the tallest bar in the original histogram. There are more bars. Each interval includes a smaller number of heights.**

GRP19

GR: Reteach, p. GRR19

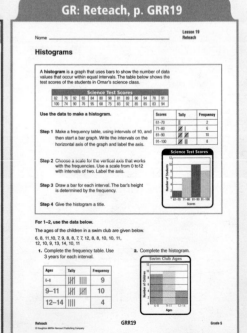

Name _____ Lesson 19
Reteach
Histograms

A **histogram** is a graph that uses bars to show the number of data values that occur within equal intervals. The table below shows the test scores of the students in Omar's science class.

Science Test Scores

Use the data to make a histogram.

Step 1 Make a frequency table, using intervals of 10, and then start a bar graph. Write the intervals on the horizontal axis of the graph and label the axis.

Step 2 Choose a scale for the vertical axis that works with the frequencies. Use a scale from 0 to 12 with intervals of two. Label the axis.

Step 3 Draw a bar for each interval. The bar's height is determined by the frequency.

Step 4 Give the histogram a title.

For 1–2, use the data below.
The ages of the children in a swim club are given below.
6, 8, 11, 10, 7, 9, 8, 8, 7, 7, 12, 8, 8, 10, 10, 11, 12, 10, 9, 13, 14, 10, 11

1. Complete the frequency table. Use 3 years for each interval.

Ages	Tally	Frequency
6–8	IIII IIII	9
9–11	IIII IIII	10
12–14	IIII	4

2. Complete the histogram.
Swim Club Ages

Reteach GRR19 Grade 6

Share and Show

For 1–3, use the data below.
The number of vacation days that each employee of a company took last summer is given below.

2, 5, 6, 11, 3, 5, 7, 8, 10, 1, 4, 6, 10, 5, 12, 15, 6, 8, 7, 14

1. Start at 1 day and use 4 days for each interval. List the intervals.

   1–4, 5–8, 9–12, 13–16

2. Complete the frequency table.

Number of Days	Tally	Frequency
1–4	IIII	**4**
5–8	LHT LHT	**10**
9–12	IIII	**4**
13–16	II	**2**

3. Complete the histogram.

On Your Own

For 4–6, use the data below.
The number of minutes that each student in Mrs. Green's class spent on homework last night is given below.

45, 30, 55, 35, 50, 48, 60, 38, 47, 56, 40, 39, 55, 65, 49, 34, 35

4. Start at 30 and use 10-minute intervals for the data. List the intervals.

   30–39, 40–49, 50–59, 60–69

5. Make a frequency table of the data. **Check students' frequency tables.**

6. Make a histogram of the data. **Check students' histograms.**

Problem Solving

7. The number of words per minute that one class of students typed is given below.

   30, 45, 28, 35, 48, 37, 41, 44, 34, 29, 25, 32, 40, 45, 39, 49

   What are reasonable intervals for the data? **Possible answer:**
   25–29, 30–34, 35–39, 40–44, 45–49

GR44

© Houghton Mifflin Harcourt Publishing Company

---

2 PRACTICE

▶ **Share and Show • Guided Practice**

Point out to students that the range of the data for Exercises 1–3 is much less than the range of data on the previous page. Therefore, a smaller interval is being used on the horizontal axis. For Exercise 3, remind students to draw the bars for each interval and to give a title for the histogram.

▶ **On Your Own • Independent Practice**

For Exercise 4, some students may forget to start with 30 when listing the 10-minute intervals. Use this opportunity to have students discuss the similarities and differences between using the different intervals.

▶ **Problem Solving** Common Core **MATHEMATICAL PRACTICES**

For Exercise 7, be sure that students use reasonable intervals.

3 SUMMARIZE

Common Core **MATHEMATICAL PRACTICES**

Essential Question

How can you use a histogram to organize data? Possible answer: Make a frequency table with reasonable intervals for the data. Choose an appropriate scale and interval for the vertical axis and list the intervals on the horizontal axis. Label each axis. Then draw a bar for each interval. Give the histogram a title.

Math Journal WRITE ▸ Math

A store had 40 customers one day. The owner recorded the amount that each customer spent. Explain whether it is more appropriate to use a histogram or a bar graph to display the data.

LESSON 20

Analyze Histograms

LESSON AT A GLANCE

Common Core Standards
Represent and interpret data.
3.MD.B.3 Draw a scaled picture graph and a scaled bar graph to represent a data set with several categories. Solve one- and two-step "how many more" and "how many less" problems using information presented in scaled bar graphs.

Summarize and describe distributions.
6.SP.B.4 Display numerical data in plots on a number line, including dot plots, histograms, and box plots.

Lesson Objective
Analyze data in a histogram.

Materials
MathBoard

GO DIGITAL

Animated Math Models

① TEACH and TALK   GO DIGITAL • Animated Math Models

▶ Unlock the Problem

Common Core MATHEMATICAL PRACTICES

Have students look at the histogram.

• **Can you tell the price that each item at the garage sale sold for? Why or why not?** No. The histogram shows only the number of items sold in each price interval, not the price of each item.

• **How can you read the value of a bar that falls halfway between two numbers on the vertical scale?** Possible answer: The value will be the number that falls in the middle or the median of the interval.

• **How can you tell how many items were sold at the garage sale?** I can find the sum of the frequencies for all of the intervals; 31 items.

• **Using the histogram, how can you calculate the least possible amount of money made during the garage sale?** Possible answer: I can find the product of the frequency and the lowest price in the range for each of the intervals and then find the sum of those products; $266.

Use **Math Talk** to check students' understanding of analyzing data in a histogram.

PG88   Planning Guide

This lesson builds on graphing data presented in Chapter 9 and prepares students for analyzing histograms taught in Grade 6.

Name _____

Analyze Histograms
Essential Question How can you analyze data in a histogram?

🔑 Unlock the Problem   Real World

The histogram shows the number of items sold at a garage sale within each price range.

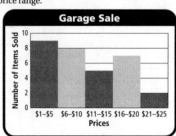

Garage Sale

! ERROR Alert
Remember to read the intervals. For some questions, you may need to combine data from two or more intervals in order to answer the question.

🔓 **How many of the items sold cost $6 to $10?**
• Find the interval labeled $6–$10.
• Find the frequency.
• The bar for $6–$10 shows that __8__ items were sold.

So, __8__ of the items sold cost $6 to $10.

🔓 **How many of the items sold cost $16 to $25?**
• Find the frequencies for the intervals labeled $16–$20 and $21–$25.
• The bar for $16–$20 shows that __7__ items were sold. The bar for $21–$25 shows that __2__ items were sold.
• Add the frequencies.

$7 + \underline{2} + \underline{9}$

So, __9__ of the items sold cost $16 to $25.

Possible explanation: You do not know how many of each item sold at a certain price.

Math Talk **Mathematical Practices**
Explain why you cannot tell from the histogram the total amount of money that was made during the garage sale.

© Houghton Mifflin Harcourt Publishing Company

Getting Ready for Grade 6   GR45

GR: Practice, p. GRP20

Name _____   **Lesson 20**
Analyze Histograms

For 1–2, use the histogram at the right.
1. Which interval has the greatest frequency?
   __10–14__

2. How many fish weighing less than 10 pounds were caught?
   __11 fish__

Number of Fish Caught on Fishing Trip

For 3–4, use the histogram at the right.
3. Which interval has the least frequency?
   __40–49__

4. How many people sent 30 or more e-mails at work yesterday?
   __8 people__

Number of E-mails Sent at Work Yesterday

Problem Solving   Real World

For 5–7, use the histogram at the right.
5. How many students sold tickets to the talent show?
   __71 students__

6. How many more students sold 10–19 tickets than sold 30–39 tickets?
   __8 more students__

Talent Show Ticket Sales

7. Can you tell from the histogram how many tickets were sold in all? Explain.
   No; Possible answer: You do not know the exact number of tickets sold by each student.

GRP20

GR: Reteach, p. GRR20

Name _____   Lesson 20
Reteach

Analyze Histograms

A histogram shows how often data occur within intervals. You can use a histogram to compare the frequency of the data within each interval.

The histogram shows the number of students in Mr. Lee's class who walked 4 miles within the range of each interval.

How many students walked between 60 and 62 minutes?
Step 1 Find the interval labeled 60–62.
Step 2 Find the frequency by reading the height of the bar. The bar ends halfway between 10 and 12. It ends at 11.

So, 11 students walked between 60 and 62 minutes.

How many students walked between 54 and 59 minutes?
Step 1 Find the intervals for the range 54–56 and 57–59.
Step 2 Find the frequency for each interval by reading the height of each bar.
54–56: 2 students
57–59: 8 students
Step 3 Add the frequencies to find the total.   2 + 8 = 10
So, 10 students walked between 54 and 59 minutes.

Minutes Students Walked

For 1–2, use the histogram at the right.
The histogram shows the number of hours of TV that students watched last week.

1. How many students watched between 10 and 14 hours of TV last week?
   __5 students__

2. How many students watched less than 10 hours of TV last week?
   __10 students__

Number of Hours of TV Last Week

Reteach   GRR20   Grade 5
© Houghton Mifflin Harcourt Publishing Company

*GR – Getting Ready Lessons and Resources (www.thinkcentral.com)

Share and Show

For 1–3, use the histogram at the right.

1. The histogram shows the number of days in one month whose temperatures were within each temperature range. On how many days was the temperature at or above 70°F?

   • List the bars that represent temperatures at or above 70°F.

   <u>70–74</u> and <u>75–79</u>

   • The frequency for interval 70–74 is <u>10</u>, and the frequency for interval 75–79 is <u>3</u>.

   • Add the frequencies. <u>10</u> + <u>3</u> + <u>13</u>

   The daily high temperature was at or above 70°F on <u>13</u> days.

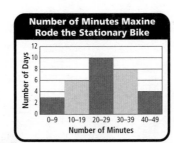

Daily High Temperatures

2. On how many days was the temperature 65°F to 69°F?
   <u>7 days</u>

3. On how many days was the temperature less than 65°F?
   <u>10 days</u>

On Your Own

For 4–5, use the histogram at the right.

4. Which interval has the greatest frequency? <u>20–29</u>

5. How many days did Maxine ride the stationary bike for 30 or more minutes? <u>12 days</u>

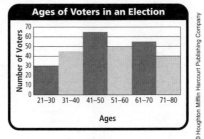

Number of Minutes Maxine Rode the Stationary Bike

Problem Solving

For 6–7, use the histogram at the right.

6. How many people voted in the election?
   <u>285 people</u>

7. How many more voters were there from ages 41–50 than from ages 21–30?
   <u>35 more voters</u>

Ages of Voters in an Election

© Houghton Mifflin Harcourt Publishing Company

GR46

---

2 PRACTICE

▶ **Share and Show • Guided Practice**

Remind students to read the questions carefully as it may be necessary for them to combine the data for two intervals in order to solve the problems.

▶ **On Your Own • Independent Practice**

For Exercise 5, have students read the question carefully to determine which interval or intervals are needed to solve the problem.

▶ **Problem Solving** Common Core **MATHEMATICAL PRACTICES**

For Exercises 6 and 7, make sure students understand how to find the amount represented by a bar that is halfway between two numbers on the vertical scale.

3 SUMMARIZE

Common Core **MATHEMATICAL PRACTICES**

Essential Question

How can you analyze data in a histogram?

Possible answer: I can find the frequency for each interval and use the frequencies to answer questions about the data.

Math Journal WRITE ▶Math

Write and answer a question using the histogram shown for Exercises 6 and 7.

Getting Ready Lessons and Resources, pp. GR47–GR48 ✓ **Checkpoint**

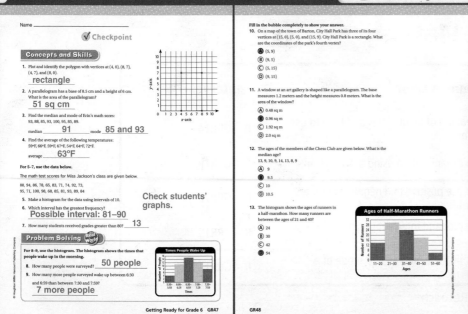

Getting Ready for Grade 6
Test

LESSONS 12 TO 20

Summative Assessment

Use the **Getting Ready Test** to assess students' progress in Getting Ready for Grade 6 Lessons 12–20.

Getting Ready Tests are provided in multiple-choice and mixed-response format in the *Getting Ready Lessons and Resources*.

 Getting Ready Test is available online.

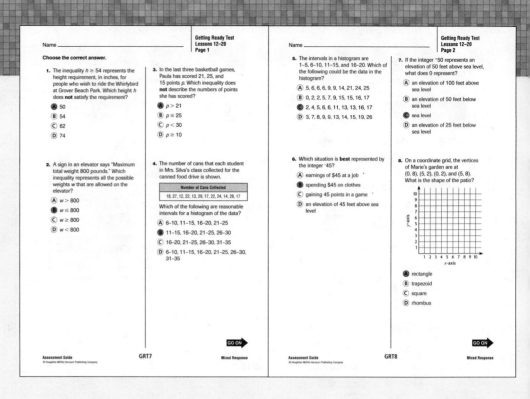

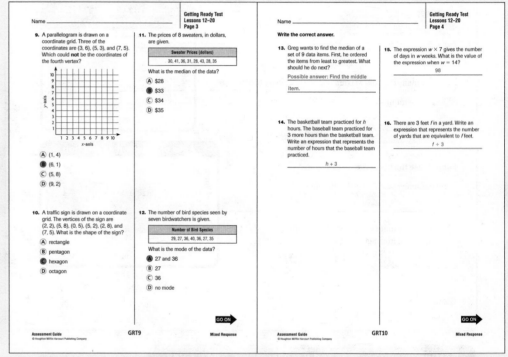

✓ Data-Driven Decision Making ▲RtI

Item	Lesson	Common Error	Intervene With
1, 2, 3	14	May not understand the meaning of inequalities and how to use inequalities to solve problems	R—GRR14
4, 5	19	May not understand how to organize data using a histogram	R—GRR19
6, 7	12	May not understand how to use positive and negative numbers to represent real-world quantities	R—GRR12
8, 9, 10	15	May not understand how to plot and interpret polygons on a coordinate grid	R—GRR15
11, 12, 13	17	May not understand how to find the median and mode of a data set	R—GRR17

Key: R—Getting Ready Lessons and Resources: Reteach

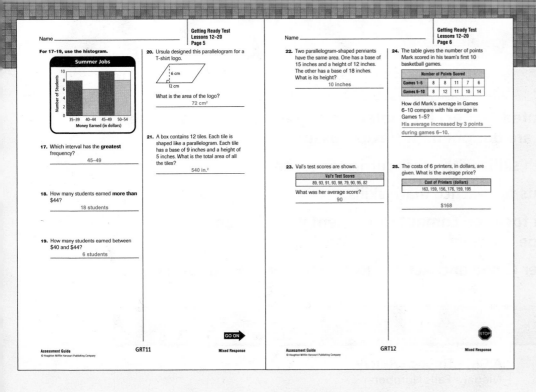

Portfolio Suggestions The portfolio represents the growth, talents, achievements, and reflections of the mathematics learner. Students might spend a short time selecting work samples for their portfolios.

You may want to have students respond to the following questions:

• What new understanding of math have I developed in the past several weeks?

• What growth in understanding or skills can I see in my work?

• What can I do to improve my understanding of math ideas?

• What would I like to learn more about?

For information about how to organize, share, and evaluate portfolios, see the *Chapter Resources*.

✓ Data-Driven Decision Making △ RtI

Item	Lesson	Common Error	Intervene With
14, 15, 16	13	May not understand how to write, interpret, and evaluate expressions	R—GRR13
17, 18, 19	20	May not understand how to analyze and interpret data presented in a histogram	R—GRR20
20, 21, 22	16	May not understand how to find the area of a parallelogram, given its base and height	R—GRR16
23, 24, 25	18	May not understand how to find the average of a data set	R—GRR18

Key: **R**—Getting Ready Lessons and Resources: Reteach

The Grab-and-Go!™ Differentiated Centers Kit contains ready-to-use readers, games, and math center activities that are designed for flexible usage.

- Readers that integrate math skills with cross-curricular content.

- Games that engage students to practice math skills.

- Math Center Activities that focus on computation, mental math, geometry, measurement, and challenge activities.

See the Grab-and-Go!™ Teacher Guide and Activity Resources for more information.

Chapter	Grade 5		
1 Place Value, Multiplication, and Expressions	Readers	A Drive Through History Niagara Falls Numbers	
	Game	What's Left?	
	Activity Cards	Card 1	Number Explosion Form Fun
		Card 11	Special 5 Amazing Areas Multiplication Relay
		Card 15	15-Minute March
2 Divide Whole Numbers	Readers	A Drive Through History Niagara Falls Numbers	
	Game	What's Left?	
	Activity Card	Card 15	Divide and Conquer 15-Minute March Decide and Divide
3 Add and Subtract Decimals	Readers	Dewey and His Decimals Halfpipe A Hundredth of a Second	
	Games	Decimal Challenge Ride the Course	
	Activity Cards	Card 4	Do We Decimal?
		Card 5	Add-A-Round Get Around! Decimal Display

Chapter	Grade 5		
4 Multiply Decimals	Reader	Doubling Every Day	
	Game	Powerful Products	
	Activity Cards	Card 4	One Form to Another
		Card 13	Dueling Decimals Market Multiplication Tic-Tac-Decimals
5 Divide Decimals	Reader	Seeking the Lowest Price	
	Game	Match Up	
	Activity Card	Card 17	D is for... Centimeter Division Grid It
6 Add and Subtract Fractions with Unlike Denominators	Readers	Fractions Add Up! Fossil Hunters Table Soccer, Anyone?	
	Games	Picture Problems What's the Difference?	
	Activity Card	Card 8	Plan a Schedule Mixed Measures Pattern Block Mix-Up

Math Center Activity Cards:

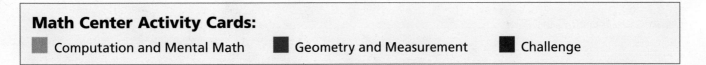

■ Computation and Mental Math ■ Geometry and Measurement ■ Challenge

Chapter	Grade 5		
7 Multiply Fractions	**Reader**	Cranking Out the Numbers	
	Game	Fraction Factors	
	Activity Cards	Card 6	Fraction Fix Up Fruitful Fractions Mixed Fractions
		Card 11	Amazing Areas
8 Divide Fractions	**Reader**	Cranking Out the Numbers	
	Game	Fraction Factors	
	Activity Card	Card 6	Fraction Fix Up
9 Algebra: Patterns and Graphing	**Readers**	Graphing Practice Is This a Career for You? Park Visitors	
	Game	It's a Toss-Up	
	Activity Cards	Card 6	Fraction Fix Up Fruitful Fractions
		Card 19	Let's Shake! Figure Out the Points What's the Point?

Chapter	Grade 5		
10 Convert Units of Measure	Readers	A Day in Dallas A Math Mix-Up	
	Game	2 Steps Forward, 1 Step Back	
	Activity Card	Card 2	Size It Up Metric! Measurement MathO Conversion Challenge
11 Geometry and Volume	Readers	Beautiful Geometry City of the Future	
	Games	Model Makers Triple Play	
	Activity Cards	Card 12	Inner Space What's in the Box?
		Card 14	Vary the Volume 3-D Construction
		Card 16	Geometry MathO Picture This
		Card 20	Protractor Practice

Math Center Activity Cards:

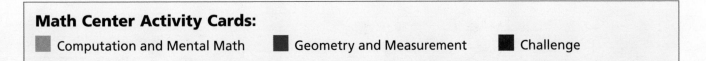

Computation and Mental Math   Geometry and Measurement   Challenge

Sequence Options

GO Math! provides the flexibility to teach the program in a different sequence. For chapters that need student background knowledge, use the list of prerequisites.

Chapter	Objectives	Prerequisites
1 Place Value, Multiplication, and Expressions COMMON CORE STATE STANDARDS 5.OA.A.1, 5.OA.A.2, 5.NBT.A.1, 5.NBT.A.2, 5.NBT.B.5, 5.NBT.B.6	• Recognize the 10 to 1 relationship among place-value positions. • Read and write whole numbers through hundred millions. • Write and evaluate repeated factors in exponent form. • Multiply by 1- and 2-digit numbers using properties and a standard algorithm. • Use multiplication to solve division problems. • Use the strategy *solve a simpler problem* to solve problems. • Write numerical expressions and evaluate numerical expressions using order of operations.	
2 Divide Whole Numbers COMMON CORE STATE STANDARDS 5.NBT.B.6, 5.NF.B.3	• Divide 3- and 4-digit dividends by 1-digit divisors using a variety of strategies. • Divide by 2-digit divisors using base-ten blocks, place value, and other strategies. • Estimate quotients using compatible numbers. • Solve division problems and decide when to write a remainder as a fraction. • Solve problems by using the strategy *draw a diagram*.	Chapter 1
3 Add and Subtract Decimals COMMON CORE STATE STANDARDS 5.NBT.A.1, 5.NBT.A.3a, 5.NBT.A.3b, 5.NBT.A.4, 5.NBT.B.7	• Model, read, and write decimals to thousandths. • Compare and order decimals to thousandths using place value. • Round decimals to any place. • Add and subtract decimals using base-ten blocks and place value. • Make reasonable estimates of decimal sums and differences. • Identify, describe, and create numerical patterns with decimals. • Solve problems using the strategy *make a table*.	
4 Multiply Decimals COMMON CORE STATE STANDARDS 5.NBT.A.2, 5.NBT.B.7	• Multiply a decimal and a whole number using drawings and place value. • Solve problems using the strategy *draw a diagram* to multiply money. • Multiply decimals using drawings and place value.	Chapters 1, 3
5 Divide Decimals COMMON CORE STATE STANDARDS 5.NBT.A.2, 5.NBT.B.7	• Estimate decimal quotients. • Divide decimals by whole numbers using drawings and place value. • Model division by decimals using drawings and place value. • Solve multistep decimal problems using the strategy *work backward*.	Chapters 2–4
6 Add and Subtract Fractions with Unlike Denominators COMMON CORE STATE STANDARDS 5.NF.A.1, 5.NF.A.2	• Add fractions with unlike denominators using models, drawings, properties, and equivalent fractions. • Subtract fractions with unlike denominators using models, drawings, and equivalent fractions. • Make reasonable estimates of fraction sums and differences. • Add and subtract mixed numbers with unlike denominators. • Identify, describe, and create numerical patterns with fractions. • Solve problems using the strategy *work backward*.	

Chapter	Objectives	Prerequisites
7 Multiply Fractions COMMON CORE STATE STANDARDS 5.NF.B.4a, 5.NF.B.4b, 5.NF.B.5a, 5.NF.B.5b, 5.NF.B.6	• Model to find the fractional part of a group. • Multiply fractions and whole numbers using models, drawings, and other strategies. • Multiply fractions using models, drawings, and other strategies. • Multiply mixed numbers using drawings and other strategies. • Relate the size of the product compared to the size of one factor when multiplying fractions less than one and greater than one. • Solve problems using the strategy *guess, check, and revise*.	Chapter 6
8 Divide Fractions COMMON CORE STATE STANDARDS 5.NF.B.3, 5.NF.B.7a, 5.NF.B.7b, 5.NF.B.7c	• Divide a whole number by a fraction and divide a fraction by a whole number using models, drawings, and other strategies. • Solve problems using the strategy *draw a diagram*. • Interpret a fraction as division and solve whole-number division problems that result in a fraction or mixed number. • Represent division by drawing diagrams and writing story problems and equations.	Chapters 6–7
9 Algebra: Patterns and Graphing COMMON CORE STATE STANDARDS 5.OA.B.3, 5.MD.B.2, 5.G.A.1, 5.G.A.2	• Make and use line plots with fractions to solve problems. • Graph and name points on a coordinate grid using ordered pairs. • Analyze and display data in a line graph. • Use two rules to generate a numerical pattern and identify the relationship between the corresponding terms in the patterns. • Solve problems using the strategy *solve a simpler problem*. • Graph the relationship between two numerical patterns on a coordinate grid.	Chapters 1–3, 6–8
10 Convert Units of Measure COMMON CORE STATE STANDARD 5.MD.A.1	• Compare, contrast, and convert customary units of length, capacity, and weight. • Convert measurement units to solve multistep problems. • Compare, contrast, and convert metric units. • Solve problems about customary and metric conversions using the strategy *make a table*. • Convert units of time to solve elapsed time problems.	Chapters 1–2, 4–5, 7–8
11 Geometry and Volume COMMON CORE STATE STANDARDS 5.MD.C.3, 5.MD.C.3a, 5.MD.C.3b, 5.MD.C.4, 5.MD.C.5a, 5.MD.C.5b, 5.MD.C.5c, 5.G.B.3, 5.G.B.4	• Classify and compare polygons, triangles, and quadrilaterals using their properties. • Solve problems using the strategy *act it out* and *make a table*. • Identify, describe, and classify three-dimensional figures. • Understand unit cubes and how they can be used to build a solid figure. • Estimate volume of a rectangular prism and find the volume of a rectangular prism by counting unit cubes and using a formula. • Find the volume of combined rectangular prisms.	Chapters 1–2

Instructional Path

Lesson	Common Core State Standards for Mathematics		Pacing
Chapter 1 Place Value, Multiplication, and Expressions			

Progress Tracker **1** 2 3 4 5 6 7 8 9 10 11

Lesson	Common Core State Standards for Mathematics		Pacing
1.1 Investigate • Place Value and Patterns	■ 5.NBT.A.1	Recognize that in a multi-digit number, a digit in one place represents 10 times as much as it represents in the place to its right and 1/10 of what it represents in the place to its left.	2 days
1.2 Place Value of Whole Numbers	■ 5.NBT.A.1	Recognize that in a multi-digit number, a digit in one place represents 10 times as much as it represents in the place to its right and 1/10 of what it represents in the place to its left.	1 day
1.3 Algebra • Properties	○ 5.OA.A.1	Use parentheses, brackets, or braces in numerical expressions, and evaluate expressions with these symbols.	1 day
1.4 Algebra • Powers of 10 and Exponents	■ 5.NBT.A.2	Explain patterns in the number of zeros of the product when multiplying a number by powers of 10, and explain patterns in the placement of the decimal point when a decimal is multiplied or divided by a power of 10. Use whole-number exponents to denote powers of 10.	1 day
1.5 Algebra • Multiplication Patterns	■ 5.NBT.A.2	Explain patterns in the number of zeros of the product when multiplying a number by powers of 10, and explain patterns in the placement of the decimal point when a decimal is multiplied or divided by a power of 10. Use whole-number exponents to denote powers of 10.	1 day
1.6 Multiply by 1-Digit Numbers	■ 5.NBT.B.5	Fluently multiply multi-digit whole numbers using the standard algorithm.	1 day
1.7 Multiply by Multi-Digit Numbers	■ 5.NBT.B.5	Fluently multiply multi-digit whole numbers using the standard algorithm.	2 days
1.8 Relate Multiplication to Division	■ 5.NBT.B.6	Find whole-number quotients of whole numbers with up to four-digit dividends and two-digit divisors, using strategies based on place value, the properties of operations, and/or the relationship between multiplication and division. Illustrate and explain the calculation by using equations, rectangular arrays, and/or area models.	2 days
1.9 Problem Solving • Multiplication and Division	■ 5.NBT.B.6	Find whole-number quotients of whole numbers with up to four-digit dividends and two-digit divisors, using strategies based on place value, the properties of operations, and/or the relationship between multiplication and division. Illustrate and explain the calculation by using equations, rectangular arrays, and/or area models.	2 days
1.10 Algebra • Numerical Expressions	○ 5.OA.A.1	Use parentheses, brackets, or braces in numerical expressions, and evaluate expressions with these symbols.	1 day
	○ 5.OA.A.2	Write simple expressions that record calculations with numbers, and interpret numerical expressions without evaluating them.	
1.11 Algebra • Evaluate Numerical Expressions	○ 5.OA.A.1	Use parentheses, brackets, or braces in numerical expressions, and evaluate expressions with these symbols.	1 day
1.12 Algebra • Grouping Symbols	○ 5.OA.A.1	Use parentheses, brackets, or braces in numerical expressions, and evaluate expressions with these symbols.	1 day

Lesson	Common Core State Standards for Mathematics		Pacing
Chapter 2 Divide Whole Numbers			
Progress Tracker 1 **2** 3 4 5 6 7 8 9 10 11			
2.1 Place the First Digit	■ 5.NBT.B.6	Find whole-number quotients of whole numbers with up to four-digit dividends and two-digit divisors, using strategies based on place value, the properties of operations, and/or the relationship between multiplication and division. Illustrate and explain the calculation by using equations, rectangular arrays, and/or area models.	1 day
2.2 Divide by 1-Digit Divisors	■ 5.NBT.B.6	Find whole-number quotients of whole numbers with up to four-digit dividends and two-digit divisors, using strategies based on place value, the properties of operations, and/or the relationship between multiplication and division. Illustrate and explain the calculation by using equations, rectangular arrays, and/or area models.	1 day
2.3 Investigate • Division with 2-Digit Divisors	■ 5.NBT.B.6	Find whole-number quotients of whole numbers with up to four-digit dividends and two-digit divisors, using strategies based on place value, the properties of operations, and/or the relationship between multiplication and division. Illustrate and explain the calculation by using equations, rectangular arrays, and/or area models.	2 days
2.4 Partial Quotients	■ 5.NBT.B.6	Find whole-number quotients of whole numbers with up to four-digit dividends and two-digit divisors, using strategies based on place value, the properties of operations, and/or the relationship between multiplication and division. Illustrate and explain the calculation by using equations, rectangular arrays, and/or area models.	1 day
2.5 Estimate with 2-Digit Divisors	■ 5.NBT.B.6	Find whole-number quotients of whole numbers with up to four-digit dividends and two-digit divisors, using strategies based on place value, the properties of operations, and/or the relationship between multiplication and division. Illustrate and explain the calculation by using equations, rectangular arrays, and/or area models.	1 day
2.6 Divide by 2-Digit Divisors	■ 5.NBT.B.6	Find whole-number quotients of whole numbers with up to four-digit dividends and two-digit divisors, using strategies based on place value, the properties of operations, and/or the relationship between multiplication and division. Illustrate and explain the calculation by using equations, rectangular arrays, and/or area models.	2 days
2.7 Interpret the Remainder	■ 5.NF.B.3	Interpret a fraction as division of the numerator by the denominator ($a/b = a \div b$). Solve word problems involving division of whole numbers leading to answers in the form of fractions or mixed numbers, e.g., by using visual fraction models or equations to represent the problem.	1 day

Chapter continued on next page ▶

■ Major Content   ☐ Supporting Content   ○ Additional Content

Lesson	Common Core State Standards for Mathematics		Pacing
Chapter 2 Divide Whole Numbers *(continued)*			
2.8 Adjust Quotients	▪ **5.NBT.B.6**	Find whole-number quotients of whole numbers with up to four-digit dividends and two-digit divisors, using strategies based on place value, the properties of operations, and/or the relationship between multiplication and division. Illustrate and explain the calculation by using equations, rectangular arrays, and/or area models.	2 days
2.9 Problem Solving • Division	▪ **5.NBT.B.6**	Find whole-number quotients of whole numbers with up to four-digit dividends and two-digit divisors, using strategies based on place value, the properties of operations, and/or the relationship between multiplication and division. Illustrate and explain the calculation by using equations, rectangular arrays, and/or area models.	2 days

Chapter 3 Add and Subtract Decimals			

Progress Tracker   1   2   3   4   5   6   7   8   9   10   11

Lesson	Common Core State Standards for Mathematics		Pacing
3.1 Investigate • Thousandths	▪ **5.NBT.A.1**	Recognize that in a multi-digit number, a digit in one place represents 10 times as much as it represents in the place to its right and 1/10 of what it represents in the place to its left.	1 day
3.2 Place Value of Decimals	▪ **5.NBT.A.3a**	Read and write decimals to thousandths using base-ten numerals, number names, and expanded form, e.g., $347.392 = 3 \times 100 + 4 \times 10 + 7 \times 1 + 3 \times (1/10) + 9 \times (1/100) + 2 \times (1/1000)$.	1 day
3.3 Compare and Order Decimals	▪ **5.NBT.A.3b**	Compare two decimals to thousandths based on meanings of the digits in each place, using $>$, $=$, and $<$ symbols to record the results of comparisons.	1 day
3.4 Round Decimals	▪ **5.NBT.A.4**	Use place value understanding to round decimals to any place.	1 day
3.5 Investigate • Decimal Addition	▪ **5.NBT.B.7**	Add, subtract, multiply, and divide decimals to hundredths, using concrete models or drawings and strategies based on place value, properties of operations, and/or the relationship between addition and subtraction; relate the strategy to a written method and explain the reasoning used.	2 days
3.6 Investigate • Decimal Subtraction	▪ **5.NBT.B.7**	Add, subtract, multiply, and divide decimals to hundredths, using concrete models or drawings and strategies based on place value, properties of operations, and/or the relationship between addition and subtraction; relate the strategy to a written method and explain the reasoning used.	1 day
3.7 Estimate Decimal Sums and Differences	▪ **5.NBT.B.7**	Add, subtract, multiply, and divide decimals to hundredths, using concrete models or drawings and strategies based on place value, properties of operations, and/or the relationship between addition and subtraction; relate the strategy to a written method and explain the reasoning used.	1 day

Chapter continued on next page ▶

Lesson	Common Core State Standards for Mathematics		Pacing
Chapter 3 Add and Subtract Decimals *(continued)*			
3.8 Add Decimals	■ 5.NBT.B.7	Add, subtract, multiply, and divide decimals to hundredths, using concrete models or drawings and strategies based on place value, properties of operations, and/or the relationship between addition and subtraction; relate the strategy to a written method and explain the reasoning used.	1 day
3.9 Subtract Decimals	■ 5.NBT.B.7	Add, subtract, multiply, and divide decimals to hundredths, using concrete models or drawings and strategies based on place value, properties of operations, and/or the relationship between addition and subtraction; relate the strategy to a written method and explain the reasoning used.	1 day
3.10 Algebra • Patterns with Decimals	■ 5.NBT.B.7	Add, subtract, multiply, and divide decimals to hundredths, using concrete models or drawings and strategies based on place value, properties of operations, and/or the relationship between addition and subtraction; relate the strategy to a written method and explain the reasoning used.	2 days
3.11 Problem Solving • Add and Subtract Money	■ 5.NBT.B.7	Add, subtract, multiply, and divide decimals to hundredths, using concrete models or drawings and strategies based on place value, properties of operations, and/or the relationship between addition and subtraction; relate the strategy to a written method and explain the reasoning used.	2 days
3.12 Choose a Method	■ 5.NBT.B.7	Add, subtract, multiply, and divide decimals to hundredths, using concrete models or drawings and strategies based on place value, properties of operations, and/or the relationship between addition and subtraction; relate the strategy to a written method and explain the reasoning used.	2 days

Chapter 4 Multiply Decimals			
Progress Tracker 1 2 3 **4** 5 6 7 8 9 10 11			
4.1 Algebra • Multiplication Patterns with Decimals	■ 5.NBT.A.2	Explain patterns in the number of zeros of the product when multiplying a number by powers of 10, and explain patterns in the placement of the decimal point when a decimal is multiplied or divided by a power of 10. Use whole-number exponents to denote powers of 10.	1 day
4.2 Investigate • Multiply Decimals and Whole Numbers	■ 5.NBT.B.7	Add, subtract, multiply, and divide decimals to hundredths, using concrete models or drawings and strategies based on place value, properties of operations, and/or the relationship between addition and subtraction; relate the strategy to a written method and explain the reasoning used.	2 days
4.3 Multiplication with Decimals and Whole Numbers	■ 5.NBT.B.7	Add, subtract, multiply, and divide decimals to hundredths, using concrete models or drawings and strategies based on place value, properties of operations, and/or the relationship between addition and subtraction; relate the strategy to a written method and explain the reasoning used.	1 day

Chapter continued on next page ▶

■ Major Content   ☐ Supporting Content   ○ Additional Content

Instructional Path   PG97D

Lesson	Common Core State Standards for Mathematics		Pacing
Chapter 4 Multiply Decimals *(continued)*			
4.4 Multiply Using Expanded Form	■ **5.NBT.B.7**	Add, subtract, multiply, and divide decimals to hundredths, using concrete models or drawings and strategies based on place value, properties of operations, and/or the relationship between addition and subtraction; relate the strategy to a written method and explain the reasoning used.	2 days
4.5 Problem Solving • Multiply Money	■ **5.NBT.B.7**	Add, subtract, multiply, and divide decimals to hundredths, using concrete models or drawings and strategies based on place value, properties of operations, and/or the relationship between addition and subtraction; relate the strategy to a written method and explain the reasoning used.	2 days
4.6 Investigate • Decimal Multiplication	■ **5.NBT.B.7**	Add, subtract, multiply, and divide decimals to hundredths, using concrete models or drawings and strategies based on place value, properties of operations, and/or the relationship between addition and subtraction; relate the strategy to a written method and explain the reasoning used.	2 days
4.7 Multiply Decimals	■ **5.NBT.B.7**	Add, subtract, multiply, and divide decimals to hundredths, using concrete models or drawings and strategies based on place value, properties of operations, and/or the relationship between addition and subtraction; relate the strategy to a written method and explain the reasoning used.	1 day
4.8 Zeros in the Product	■ **5.NBT.B.7**	Add, subtract, multiply, and divide decimals to hundredths, using concrete models or drawings and strategies based on place value, properties of operations, and/or the relationship between addition and subtraction; relate the strategy to a written method and explain the reasoning used.	1 day

Lesson	Common Core State Standards for Mathematics		Pacing
Chapter 5 Divide Decimals			
Progress Tracker 1 2 3 4 5 6 7 8 9 10 11			
5.1 Algebra • Division Patterns with Decimals	■ **5.NBT.A.2**	Explain patterns in the number of zeros of the product when multiplying a number by powers of 10, and explain patterns in the placement of the decimal point when a decimal is multiplied or divided by a power of 10. Use whole-number exponents to denote powers of 10.	1 day
5.2 Investigate • Divide Decimals by Whole Numbers	■ **5.NBT.B.7**	Add, subtract, multiply, and divide decimals to hundredths, using concrete models or drawings and strategies based on place value, properties of operations, and/or the relationship between addition and subtraction; relate the strategy to a written method and explain the reasoning used.	2 days
5.3 Estimate Quotients	■ **5.NBT.B.7**	Add, subtract, multiply, and divide decimals to hundredths, using concrete models or drawings and strategies based on place value, properties of operations, and/or the relationship between addition and subtraction; relate the strategy to a written method and explain the reasoning used.	1 day

Chapter continued on next page ▶

Lesson		Common Core State Standards for Mathematics	Pacing
Chapter 5 Divide Decimals *(continued)*			
5.4 Division of Decimals by Whole Numbers	■ **5.NBT.B.7**	Add, subtract, multiply, and divide decimals to hundredths, using concrete models or drawings and strategies based on place value, properties of operations, and/or the relationship between addition and subtraction; relate the strategy to a written method and explain the reasoning used.	1 day
5.5 Investigate • Decimal Division	■ **5.NBT.B.7**	Add, subtract, multiply, and divide decimals to hundredths, using concrete models or drawings and strategies based on place value, properties of operations, and/or the relationship between addition and subtraction; relate the strategy to a written method and explain the reasoning used.	2 days
5.6 Divide Decimals	■ **5.NBT.B.7**	Add, subtract, multiply, and divide decimals to hundredths, using concrete models or drawings and strategies based on place value, properties of operations, and/or the relationship between addition and subtraction; relate the strategy to a written method and explain the reasoning used.	2 days
5.7 Write Zeros in the Dividend	■ **5.NBT.B.7**	Add, subtract, multiply, and divide decimals to hundredths, using concrete models or drawings and strategies based on place value, properties of operations, and/or the relationship between addition and subtraction; relate the strategy to a written method and explain the reasoning used.	1 day
5.8 Problem Solving • Decimal Operations	■ **5.NBT.B.7**	Add, subtract, multiply, and divide decimals to hundredths, using concrete models or drawings and strategies based on place value, properties of operations, and/or the relationship between addition and subtraction; relate the strategy to a written method and explain the reasoning used.	2 days

Chapter 6 Add and Subtract Fractions with Unlike Denominators			
Progress Tracker 1 2 3 4 5 **6** 7 8 9 10 11			
6.1 Investigate • Addition with Unlike Denominators	■ **5.NF.A.1** ■ **5.NF.A.2**	Add and subtract fractions with unlike denominators (including mixed numbers) by replacing given fractions with equivalent fractions in such a way as to produce an equivalent sum or difference of fractions with like denominators. Solve word problems involving addition and subtraction of fractions referring to the same whole, including cases of unlike denominators, e.g., by using visual fraction models or equations to represent the problem. Use benchmark fractions and number sense of fractions to estimate mentally and assess the reasonableness of answers.	2 days
6.2 Investigate • Subtraction with Unlike Denominators	■ **5.NF.A.2**	Solve word problems involving addition and subtraction of fractions referring to the same whole, including cases of unlike denominators, e.g., by using visual fraction models or equations to represent the problem. Use benchmark fractions and number sense of fractions to estimate mentally and assess the reasonableness of answers.	2 days

Chapter continued on next page ▶

■ Major Content ◻ Supporting Content ◯ Additional Content

Lesson		Common Core State Standards for Mathematics	Pacing
Chapter 6 Add and Subtract Fractions with Unlike Denominators *(continued)*			
6.3 Estimate Fraction Sums and Differences	◼ 5.NF.A.2	Solve word problems involving addition and subtraction of fractions referring to the same whole, including cases of unlike denominators, e.g., by using visual fraction models or equations to represent the problem. Use benchmark fractions and number sense of fractions to estimate mentally and assess the reasonableness of answers.	1 day
6.4 Common Denominators and Equivalent Fractions	◼ 5.NF.A.1	Add and subtract fractions with unlike denominators (including mixed numbers) by replacing given fractions with equivalent fractions in such a way as to produce an equivalent sum or difference of fractions with like denominators.	1 day
6.5 Add and Subtract Fractions	◼ 5.NF.A.1	Add and subtract fractions with unlike denominators (including mixed numbers) by replacing given fractions with equivalent fractions in such a way as to produce an equivalent sum or difference of fractions with like denominators.	1 day
6.6 Add and Subtract Mixed Numbers	◼ 5.NF.A.1	Add and subtract fractions with unlike denominators (including mixed numbers) by replacing given fractions with equivalent fractions in such a way as to produce an equivalent sum or difference of fractions with like denominators.	1 day
6.7 Subtract with Renaming	◼ 5.NF.A.1	Add and subtract fractions with unlike denominators (including mixed numbers) by replacing given fractions with equivalent fractions in such a way as to produce an equivalent sum or difference of fractions with like denominators.	2 days
6.8 Algebra • Patterns with Fractions	◼ 5.NF.A.1	Add and subtract fractions with unlike denominators (including mixed numbers) by replacing given fractions with equivalent fractions in such a way as to produce an equivalent sum or difference of fractions with like denominators.	1 day
6.9 Problem Solving • Practice Addition and Subtraction	◼ 5.NF.A.2	Solve word problems involving addition and subtraction of fractions referring to the same whole, including cases of unlike denominators, e.g., by using visual fraction models or equations to represent the problem. Use benchmark fractions and number sense of fractions to estimate mentally and assess the reasonableness of answers.	1 day
6.10 Algebra • Use Properties of Addition	◼ 5.NF.A.1	Add and subtract fractions with unlike denominators (including mixed numbers) by replacing given fractions with equivalent fractions in such a way as to produce an equivalent sum or difference of fractions with like denominators.	2 days

Chapter 7 Multiply Fractions			
Progress Tracker 1 2 3 4 5 6 **7** 8 9 10 11			
7.1 Find Part of a Group	◼ 5.NF.B.4a	Interpret the product $(a/b) \times q$ as a parts of a partition of q into b equal parts; equivalently, as the result of a sequence of operations $a \times q \div b$.	1 day
7.2 Investigate • Multiply Fractions and Whole Numbers	◼ 5.NF.B.4a	Interpret the product $(a/b) \times q$ as a parts of a partition of q into b equal parts; equivalently, as the result of a sequence of operations $a \times q \div b$.	2 days

Chapter continued on next page ▶

Lesson	Common Core State Standards for Mathematics		Pacing
Chapter 7 Multiply Fractions (*continued*)			
7.3 Fraction and Whole Number Multiplication	■ **5.NF.B.4a**	Interpret the product (*a/b*) × *q* as a parts of a partition of *q* into *b* equal parts; equivalently, as the result of a sequence of operations *a* × *q* ÷ *b*.	1 day
7.4 Investigate • Multiply Fractions	■ **5.NF.B.4a**	Interpret the product (*a/b*) × *q* as a parts of a partition of *q* into *b* equal parts; equivalently, as the result of a sequence of operations *a* × *q* ÷ *b*.	2 days
	■ **5.NF.B.4b**	Find the area of a rectangle with fractional side lengths by tiling it with unit squares of the appropriate unit fraction side lengths, and show that the area is the same as would be found by multiplying the side lengths. Multiply fractional side lengths to find areas of rectangles, and represent fraction products as rectangular areas.	
7.5 Compare Fraction Factors and Products	■ **5.NF.B.5a**	Comparing the size of a product to the size of one factor on the basis of the size of the other factor, without performing the indicated multiplication.	1 day
	■ **5.NF.B.5b**	Explaining why multiplying a given number by a fraction greater than 1 results in a product greater than the given number (recognizing multiplication by whole numbers greater than 1 as a familiar case); explaining why multiplying a given number by a fraction less than 1 results in a product smaller than the given number; and relating the principle of fraction equivalence *a/b* = (*n* × *a*)/(*n* × *b*) to the effect of multiplying *a/b* by 1.	
7.6 Fraction Multiplication	■ **5.NF.B.4a**	Interpret the product (*a/b*) × *q* as a parts of a partition of *q* into *b* equal parts; equivalently, as the result of a sequence of operations *a* × *q* ÷ *b*.	1 day
	■ **5.NF.B.5b**	Explaining why multiplying a given number by a fraction greater than 1 results in a product greater than the given number (recognizing multiplication by whole numbers greater than 1 as a familiar case); explaining why multiplying a given number by a fraction less than 1 results in a product smaller than the given number; and relating the principle of fraction equivalence *a/b* = (*n* × *a*)/(*n* × *b*) to the effect of multiplying *a/b* by 1.	
7.7 Investigate • Area and Mixed Numbers	■ **5.NF.B.4b**	Find the area of a rectangle with fractional side lengths by tiling it with unit squares of the appropriate unit fraction side lengths, and show that the area is the same as would be found by multiplying the side lengths. Multiply fractional side lengths to find areas of rectangles, and represent fraction products as rectangular areas.	2 days
7.8 Compare Mixed Number Factors and Products	■ **5.NF.B.5a**	Comparing the size of a product to the size of one factor on the basis of the size of the other factor, without performing the indicated multiplication.	1 day
	■ **5.NF.B.5b**	Explaining why multiplying a given number by a fraction greater than 1 results in a product greater than the given number (recognizing multiplication by whole numbers greater than 1 as a familiar case); explaining why multiplying a given number by a fraction less than 1 results in a product smaller than the given number; and relating the principle of fraction equivalence *a/b* = (*n* × *a*)/(*n* × *b*) to the effect of multiplying *a/b* by 1.	

Chapter continued on next page ▶

■ Major Content   □ Supporting Content   ○ Additional Content

Lesson	Common Core State Standards for Mathematics		Pacing
Chapter 7 Multiply Fractions (*continued*)			
7.9 Multiply Mixed Numbers	▇ **5.NF.B.6**	Solve real world problems involving multiplication of fractions and mixed numbers, e.g., by using visual fraction models or equations to represent the problem.	1 day
7.10 Problem Solving • Find Unknown Lengths	▇ **5.NF.B.4b**	Find the area of a rectangle with fractional side lengths by tiling it with unit squares of the appropriate unit fraction side lengths, and show that the area is the same as would be found by multiplying the side lengths. Multiply fractional side lengths to find areas of rectangles, and represent fraction products as rectangular areas.	2 days
	▇ **5.NF.B.6**	Solve real world problems involving multiplication of fractions and mixed numbers, e.g., by using visual fraction models or equations to represent the problem.	

Chapter 8 Divide Fractions			

Progress Tracker	1	2	3	4	5	6	7	**8**	9	10	11

Lesson	Common Core State Standards for Mathematics		Pacing
8.1 Investigate • Divide Fractions and Whole Numbers	▇ **5.NF.B.7a**	Interpret division of a unit fraction by a non-zero whole number, and compute such quotients.	2 days
	▇ **5.NF.B.7b**	Interpret division of a whole number by a unit fraction, and compute such quotients.	
8.2 Problem Solving • Use Multiplication	▇ **5.NF.B.7b**	Interpret division of a whole number by a unit fraction, and compute such quotients.	2 days
8.3 Connect Fractions to Division	▇ **5.NF.B.3**	Interpret a fraction as division of the numerator by the denominator ($a/b = a \div b$). Solve word problems involving division of whole numbers leading to answers in the form of fractions or mixed numbers, e.g., by using visual fraction models or equations to represent the problem.	1 day
8.4 Fraction and Whole-Number Division	▇ **5.NF.B.7c**	Solve real world problems involving division of unit fractions by non-zero whole numbers and division of whole numbers by unit fractions, e.g., by using visual fraction models and equations to represent the problem.	2 days
8.5 Interpret Division with Fractions	▇ **5.NF.B.7a**	Interpret division of a unit fraction by a non-zero whole number, and compute such quotients.	2 days
	▇ **5.NF.B.7b**	Interpret division of a whole number by a unit fraction, and compute such quotients.	

Lesson		Common Core State Standards for Mathematics	Pacing
Chapter 9 Algebra: Patterns and Graphing			

Progress Tracker 1 2 3 4 5 6 7 8 **9** 10 11

Lesson		Common Core State Standards for Mathematics	Pacing
9.1 Line Plots	☐ 5.MD.B.2	Make a line plot to display a data set of measurements in fractions of a unit (1/2, 1/4, 1/8). Use operations on fractions for this grade to solve problems involving information presented in line plots.	1 day
9.2 Ordered Pairs	○ 5.G.A.1	Use a pair of perpendicular number lines, called axes, to define a coordinate system, with the intersection of the lines (the origin) arranged to coincide with the 0 on each line and a given point in the plane located by using an ordered pair of numbers, called its coordinates. Understand that the first number indicates how far to travel from the origin in the direction of one axis, and the second number indicates how far to travel in the direction of the second axis, with the convention that the names of the two axes and the coordinates correspond (e.g., *x*-axis and *x*-coordinate, *y*-axis and *y*-coordinate).	1 day
9.3 Investigate • Graph Data	○ 5.G.A.2	Represent real world and mathematical problems by graphing points in the first quadrant of the coordinate plane, and interpret coordinate values of points in the context of the situation.	1 day
9.4 Line Graphs	○ 5.G.A.2	Represent real world and mathematical problems by graphing points in the first quadrant of the coordinate plane, and interpret coordinate values of points in the context of the situation.	1 day
9.5 Numerical Patterns	○ 5.OA.B.3	Generate two numerical patterns using two given rules. Identify apparent relationships between corresponding terms. Form ordered pairs consisting of corresponding terms from the two patterns, and graph the ordered pairs on a coordinate plane.	1 day
9.6 Problem Solving • Find a Rule	○ 5.OA.B.3	Generate two numerical patterns using two given rules. Identify apparent relationships between corresponding terms. Form ordered pairs consisting of corresponding terms from the two patterns, and graph the ordered pairs on a coordinate plane.	1 day
9.7 Graph and Analyze Relationships	○ 5.OA.B.3	Generate two numerical patterns using two given rules. Identify apparent relationships between corresponding terms. Form ordered pairs consisting of corresponding terms from the two patterns, and graph the ordered pairs on a coordinate plane.	1 day

Chapter 10 Convert Units of Measure			

Progress Tracker 1 2 3 4 5 6 7 8 9 **10** 11

Lesson		Common Core State Standards for Mathematics	Pacing
10.1 Customary Length	☐ 5.MD.A.1	Convert among different-sized standard measurement units within a given measurement system (e.g., convert 5 cm to 0.05 m), and use these conversions in solving multi-step, real world problems.	1 day
10.2 Customary Capacity	☐ 5.MD.A.1	Convert among different-sized standard measurement units within a given measurement system (e.g., convert 5 cm to 0.05 m), and use these conversions in solving multi-step, real world problems.	1 day

■ Major Content   ☐ Supporting Content   ○ Additional Content

Chapter continued on next page ▶

Lesson	Common Core State Standards for Mathematics		Pacing
Chapter 10 Convert Units of Measure *(continued)*			
10.3 Weight	☐ **5.MD.A.1**	Convert among different-sized standard measurement units within a given measurement system (e.g., convert 5 cm to 0.05 m), and use these conversions in solving multi-step, real world problems.	1 day
10.4 Multistep Measurement Problems	☐ **5.MD.A.1**	Convert among different-sized standard measurement units within a given measurement system (e.g., convert 5 cm to 0.05 m), and use these conversions in solving multi-step, real world problems.	1 day
10.5 Metric Measures	☐ **5.MD.A.1**	Convert among different-sized standard measurement units within a given measurement system (e.g., convert 5 cm to 0.05 m), and use these conversions in solving multi-step, real world problems.	1 day
10.6 Problem Solving • Customary and Metric Conversions	☐ **5.MD.A.1**	Convert among different-sized standard measurement units within a given measurement system (e.g., convert 5 cm to 0.05 m), and use these conversions in solving multi-step, real world problems.	1 day
10.7 Elapsed Time	☐ **5.MD.A.1**	Convert among different-sized standard measurement units within a given measurement system (e.g., convert 5 cm to 0.05 m), and use these conversions in solving multi-step, real world problems.	1 day

Chapter 11 Geometry and Volume			

Progress Tracker   1   2   3   4   5   6   7   8   9   10   **11**

Lesson	Common Core State Standards for Mathematics		Pacing
11.1 Polygons	○ **5.G.B.3**	Understand that attributes belonging to a category of two dimensional figures also belong to all subcategories of that category.	1 day
	○ **5.G.B.4**	Classify two-dimensional figures in a hierarchy based on properties.	
11.2 Triangles	○ **5.G.B.3**	Understand that attributes belonging to a category of two dimensional figures also belong to all subcategories of that category.	1 day
	○ **5.G.B.4**	Classify two-dimensional figures in a hierarchy based on properties.	
11.3 Quadrilaterals	○ **5.G.B.3**	Understand that attributes belonging to a category of two dimensional figures also belong to all subcategories of that category.	1 day
	○ **5.G.B.4**	Classify two-dimensional figures in a hierarchy based on properties.	
11.4 Three-Dimensional Figures	■ **5.MD.C.3**	Recognize volume as an attribute of solid figures and understand concepts of volume measurement.	1 day
11.5 Investigate • Unit Cubes and Solid Figures	■ **5.MD.C.3a**	A cube with side length 1 unit, called a "unit cube," is said to have "one cubic unit" of volume, and can be used to measure volume.	1 day
11.6 Investigate • Understand Volume	■ **5.MD.C.3b**	A solid figure which can be packed without gaps or overlaps using n unit cubes is said to have a volume of *n* cubic units.	1 day
	■ **5.MD.C.4**	Measure volumes by counting unit cubes, using cubic cm, cubic in, cubic ft, and improvised units.	
11.7 Investigate • Estimate Volume	■ **5.MD.C.4**	Measure volumes by counting unit cubes, using cubic cm, cubic in, cubic ft, and improvised units.	1 day

Chapter continued on next page ▶

Lesson	Common Core State Standards for Mathematics		Pacing
Chapter 11 **Geometry and Volume** *(continued)*			
11.8 Volume of Rectangular Prisms	■ **5.MD.C.5a**	Find the volume of a right rectangular prism with whole-number side lengths by packing it with unit cubes, and show that the volume is the same as would be found by multiplying the edge lengths, equivalently by multiplying the height by the area of the base. Represent threefold whole-number products as volumes, e.g., to represent the associative property of multiplication.	1 day
	■ **5.MD.C.5b**	Apply the formulas $V = l \times w \times h$ and $V = b \times h$ for rectangular prisms to find volumes of right rectangular prisms with whole number edge lengths in the context of solving real world and mathematical problems.	
11.9 Algebra • Apply Volume Formulas	■ **5.MD.C.5a**	Find the volume of a right rectangular prism with whole-number side lengths by packing it with unit cubes, and show that the volume is the same as would be found by multiplying the edge lengths, equivalently by multiplying the height by the area of the base. Represent threefold whole-number products as volumes, e.g., to represent the associative property of multiplication.	1 day
	■ **5.MD.C.5b**	Apply the formulas $V = l \times w \times h$ and $V = b \times h$ for rectangular prisms to find volumes of right rectangular prisms with whole number edge lengths in the context of solving real world and mathematical problems.	
11.10 Problem Solving • Compare Volumes	■ **5.MD.C.5b**	Apply the formulas $V = l \times w \times h$ and $V = b \times$ h for rectangular prisms to find volumes of right rectangular prisms with whole number edge lengths in the context of solving real world and mathematical problems.	2 days
11.11 Find Volume of Composed Figures	■ **5.MD.C.5c**	Recognize volume as additive. Find volumes of solid figures composed of two non-overlapping right rectangular prisms by adding the volumes of the non-overlapping parts, applying this technique to solve real world problems.	2 days

■ Major Content   ☐ Supporting Content   ◯ Additional Content

Path to Fluency: Kindergarten through Grade 6

GO Math! includes a plan for helping students achieve fluency with the Common Core State Standards that are suggested for each grade. This plan provides targeted instruction and practice in the Student Edition, Teacher Edition, Teacher Resource Book, Strategies and Practice for Skills and Facts Fluency, Personal Math Trainer, and Animated Math Models. Individual components will aid students in building proficiency. Together, they offer a unique suite of materials to help all students achieve mastery.

Fluency and Memorization for Basic Facts

Grade	Standards	Resources
Kindergarten Fluency	**K.OA.A.5** Fluently add and subtract within 5.	• Games (Student Edition) • Fluency Standard Lessons (Student Edition) • Fluency Builder (Teacher Edition) • Strategies and Practice for Skills and Facts Fluency—Primary, GK–3 • Teacher Resource Book • HMH Mega Math • Personal Math Trainer: Standards Quizzes • Animated Math Models
Grade 1 Fluency	**1.OA.C.6** Add and subtract within 20, demonstrating fluency for addition and subtraction within 10. Use strategies such as counting on; making ten; decomposing a number leading to a ten; using the relationship between addition and subtraction; and creating equivalent but easier or known sums.	• Games (Student Edition) • Fluency Standard Lessons (Student Edition) • Fluency Builder (Teacher Edition) • Strategies and Practice for Skills and Facts Fluency—Primary, GK–3 • Teacher Resource Book • HMH Mega Math • Personal Math Trainer: Standards Quizzes • Animated Math Models
Grade 2 Memorization	**2.OA.B.2** Fluently add and subtract within 20 using mental strategies.	• Games (Student Edition) • Fluency Standard Lessons (Student Edition) • Fluency Builder (Teacher Edition) • Strategies and Practice for Skills and Facts Fluency—Primary, GK–3 • Teacher Resource Book • HMH Mega Math • Personal Math Trainer: Standards Quizzes • Animated Math Models
Grade 3 Memorization	**3.OA.C.7** Fluently multiply and divide within 100, using strategies such as the relationship between multiplication and division or properties of operations. By the end of Grade 3, know from memory all products of two one-digit numbers.	• Fluency Standard Lessons (Student Edition) • Fluency Builder (Teacher Edition) • Strategies and Practice for Skills and Facts Fluency—Primary, GK–3 • Strategies and Practice for Skills and Facts Fluency—Intermediate, G3–6 • Teacher Resource Book • HMH Mega Math • Personal Math Trainer: Standards Quizzes • Animated Math Models
Grades 3, 4, 5, and 6 Intervention	For those students who still need additional time for memorizing basic facts.	• Fluency Builder (Teacher Edition) • Strategies and Practice for Skills and Facts Fluency—Intermediate, G3–6 • Teacher Resource Book • HMH Mega Math • Personal Math Trainer: Standards Quizzes • Animated Math Models

Fluency for Operations with Multi-digit Numbers

Grade	Standards	Resources
Grade 2 Fluency	**2.NBT.B.5** Fluently add and subtract within 100 using strategies based on place value, properties of operations, and/or the relationship between addition and subtraction.	• Games (Student Edition) • Fluency Standard Lessons (Student Edition) • Fluency Builder (Teacher Edition) • HMH Mega Math • Personal Math Trainer: Standards Quizzes • Animated Math Models
Grade 3 Fluency	**3.NBT.A.2** Fluently add and subtract within 1000 using strategies and algorithms based on place value, properties of operations, and/or the relationship between addition and subtraction.	• Fluency Standard Lessons (Student Edition) • Fluency Builder (Teacher Edition) • Strategies and Practice for Skills and Facts Fluency—Intermediate, G3–6 • HMH Mega Math • Personal Math Trainer: Standards Quizzes • Animated Math Models
Grade 4 Fluency	**4.NBT.B.4** Fluently add and subtract multi-digit whole numbers using the standard algorithm.	• Fluency Standard Lessons (Student Edition) • Fluency Builder (Teacher Edition) • Strategies and Practice for Skills and Facts Fluency—Intermediate, G3–6 • HMH Mega Math • Personal Math Trainer: Standards Quizzes • Animated Math Models
Grade 5 Fluency	**5.NBT.B.5** Fluently multiply multi-digit whole numbers using the standard algorithm.	• Fluency Standard Lessons (Student Edition) • Fluency Builder (Teacher Edition) • Strategies and Practice for Skills and Facts Fluency—Intermediate, G3–6 • HMH Mega Math • Personal Math Trainer: Standards Quizzes • Animated Math Models
Grade 6 Fluency	**6.NS.B.2** Fluently divide multi-digit numbers using the standard algorithm. **6.NS.B.3** Fluently add, subtract, multiply, and divide multi-digit decimals using the standard algorithm for each operation.	• Fluency Standard Lessons (Student Edition) • Fluency Builder (Teacher Edition) • Strategies and Practice for Skills and Facts Fluency—Intermediate, G3–6 • Fluency Builders (Teacher Resource Book) • HMH Mega Math Personal Math Trainer: Standards Quizzes • Animated Math Models

Standards for Mathematical Practices

Student Edition and Teacher Edition Pages

MP1	Make sense of problems and persevere in solving them.	In most Student Edition lessons. Some examples are: 14, 37, 56, 114, 119, 132, 138, 202, 213, 222, 258, 271, 303, 311, 375, 392, 401, 478, 597, 676, 693
		In most Teacher Edition lessons. Some examples are: *37, 93, 221, 257, 303, 389, 536, 643*
MP2	Reason abstractly and quantitatively.	In most Student Edition lessons. Some examples are: 20, 58, 93, 160, 182, 196, 201, 221, 266, 304, 311, 317, 325, 336, 371, 376, 383, 404, 435, 472, 506, 519, 534, 613, 677
		In most Teacher Edition lessons. Some examples are: *39, 221, 310, 369, 472, 503, 517, 519, 533, 613, 677*
MP3	Construct viable arguments and critique the reasoning of others.	In most Student Edition lessons. Some examples are: 30, 52, 62, 69, 101, 127, 170, 268, 274, 359, 468, 548
		In most Teacher Edition lessons. Some examples are: 67, *116, 268, 439, 491, 511, 548, 670, 699*
MP4	Model with mathematics.	In most Student Edition lessons. Some examples are: 61, 73, 100, 126, 151, 239, 258, 305, 351, 430, 518, 539, 546, 552, 618
		In most Teacher Edition lessons. Some examples are: *43, 251, 257, 424, 459, 533, 539, 552, 565, 617*
MP5	Use appropriate tools strategically.	In most Student Edition lessons. Some examples are: 5, 99, 152, 183, 189, 219, 292, 297, 317, 329, 351, 422, 427, 459, 494, 637, 663
		In most Teacher Edition lessons. Some examples are: *23, 151, 219, 265, 294, 421, 439, 466, 494, 511, 663*
MP6	Attend to precision.	In most Student Edition lessons. Some examples are: 44, 50, 87, 99, 132, 166, 175, 191, 246, 253, 278, 319, 330, 385, 421, 428, 497, 503, 585, 591, 604, 624, 643, 657, 664, 670, 683, 702
		In most Teacher Edition lessons. Some examples are: *43, 49, 89, 291, 446, 477, 540, 591, 603, 663*
MP7	Look for and make use of structure.	In most Student Edition lessons. Some examples are: 7, 24, 51, 133, 152, 157, 207, 293, 338, 397, 409, 560, 568, 571, 618, 649
		In most Teacher Edition lessons. Some examples are: *5, 169, 209, 233, 291, 323, 363, 559, 562, 646*
MP8	Look for and express regularity in repeated reasoning.	In most Student Edition lessons. Some examples are: 17, 29, 106, 121, 181, 209, 272, 331, 407, 546, 645, 655
		In most Teacher Edition lessons. Some examples are: *17, 29, 106, 181, 357, 395, 545, 559, 611, 637, 649*

Domain: Operations and Algebraic Thinking		Student Edition and Teacher Edition Pages
Cluster A: Write and interpret numerical expressions.		
5.OA.A.1	Use parentheses, brackets, or braces in numerical expressions, and evaluate expressions with these symbols.	*17A–17B*, 17–20, *61A–61B*, 61–64, *67A–67B*, *67–70*, *73A–73B*, 73–76 See Also: *533A–533B*, 533–536
5.OA.A.2	Write simple expressions that record calculations with numbers, and interpret numerical expressions without evaluating them.	*61A–61B*, 61–64 See Also: *369A–369B*, 369–372
Cluster B: Analyze patterns and relationships.		
5.OA.B.3	Generate two numerical patterns using two given rules. Identify apparent relationships between corresponding terms. Form ordered pairs consisting of corresponding terms from the two patterns, and graph the ordered pairs on a coordinate plane.	*559A–559B*, 559–562, *565A–565B*, 565–568, *571A–571B*, 571–475

Domain: Number and Operations in Base Ten		Student Edition and Teacher Edition Pages
Cluster A: Understand the place value system.		
5.NBT.A.1	Recognize that in a multi-digit number, a digit in one place represents 10 times as much as it represents in the place to its right and 1/10 of what it represents in the place to its left.	*5A–5B*, 5–8, *11A–11B*, 11–14, *151A–151B*, 151–154 See Also: *157A–157B*, 157–160
5.NBT.A.2	Explain patterns in the number of zeros of the product when multiplying a number by powers of 10, and explain patterns in the placement of the decimal point when a decimal is multiplied or divided by a power of 10. Use whole-number exponents to denote powers of 10.	*23A–23B*, 23–26, *29A–29B*, 29–32, *233A–233B*, 233–236, *291A–291B*, 291–294 See Also: *245A–245B*, 245–248, *251A–251B*, 251–254, *271A–271B*, 271–274, *277A–277B*, 277–280, *323A–323B*, 323–326
5.NBT.A.3	Read, write, and compare decimals to thousandths.	
	a. Read and write decimals to thousandths using base-ten numerals, number names, and expanded form, e.g., $347.392 = 3 \times 100 + 4 \times 10 + 7 \times 1 + 3 \times (1/10) + 9 \times (1/100) + 2 \times (1/1000)$.	*157A–157B*, 157–160 See Also: *151A–151B*, 151–154
	b. Compare two decimals to thousandths based on meanings of the digits in each place, using >, =, and < symbols to record the results of comparisons.	*163A–163B*, 163–166
5.NBT.A.4	Use place value understanding to round decimals to any place.	*169A–169B*, 169–172

Pages only in Teacher Edition are shown in italics.

Domain continued on next page ▶

Domain: Number and Operations in Base Ten *(continued)*

■ Cluster B: Perform operations with multi-digit whole numbers and with decimals to hundredths.

5.NBT.B.5	Fluently multiply multi-digit whole numbers using the standard algorithm.	*37A–37B*, 37–40, *43A–43B*, 43–46
5.NBT.B.6	Find whole-number quotients of whole numbers with up to four-digit dividends and two-digit divisors, using strategies based on place value, the properties of operations, and/or the relationship between multiplication and division. Illustrate and explain the calculation by using equations, rectangular arrays, and/or area models.	*49A–49B*, 49–52, *55A–55B*, 55–58, *87A–87B*, *87–90*, *93A–93B*, 93–96, *99A–99B*, 99–102, *105A–105B*, 105–108, *113A–113B*, 113–116, *119A–119B*, 119–122, *131A–131B*, 131–134, *137A–137B*, 137–140 See Also: *125A–125B*, 125–128
5.NBT.B.7	Add, subtract, multiply, and divide decimals to hundredths, using concrete models or drawings and strategies based on place value, properties of operations, and/or the relationship between addition and subtraction; relate the strategy to a written method and explain the reasoning used.	*175A–175B*, 175–178, *181A–181B*, 181–184, *189A–189B*, 189–192, *195A–195B*, 195–198, *201A–201B*, 201–204, *207A–207B*, 207–210, *213A–213B*, 213–216, *219A–219B*, 219–222, *239A–239B*, 239–242, *245A–245B*, 245–248, *251A–251B*, 251–254, *257A–257B*, 257–260, *265A–265B*, 265–268, *271A–271B*, 271–274, *277A–277B*, 277–280, *297A–297B*, 297–300, *303A–303B*, 303–306, *309A–309B*, 309–342, *317A–317B*, 317–320, *323A–323B*, 323–326, *329A–329B*, 329–332, *335A–335B*, 335–338 See Also: *233A–233B*, 233–236

Domain: Number and Operations—Fractions

■ Cluster A: Use equivalent fractions as a strategy to add and subtract fractions.

5.NF.A.1	Add and subtract fractions with unlike denominators (including mixed numbers) by replacing given fractions with equivalent fractions in such a way as to produce an equivalent sum or difference of fractions with like denominators.	*351A–351B*, 351–354, *369A–369B*, 369–372, *375A–375B*, 375–378, *383A–383B*, 383–386, *389A–389B*, 389–392, *395A–395B*, 395–398, *407A–407B*, 407–410 See Also: *401A–401B*, 401–404
5.NF.A.2	Solve word problems involving addition and subtraction of fractions referring to the same whole, including cases of unlike denominators, e.g., by using visual fraction models or equations to represent the problem. Use benchmark fractions and number sense of fractions to estimate mentally and assess the reasonableness of answers.	*351A–351B*, 351–354, *357A–357B*, 357–360, *363A–363B*, 363–366, *401A–401B*, 401–404 See Also: *375A–375B*, 375–378, *383A–383B*, 383–386, *389A–389B*, 389–392

Domain continued on next page ▶

Domain: Number and Operations—Fractions *(continued)*		**Student Edition and Teacher Edition Pages**
Cluster B: Apply and extend previous understandings of multiplication and division.		
5.NF.B.3	Interpret a fraction as division of the numerator by the denominator ($a/b = a \div b$). Solve word problems involving division of whole numbers leading to answers in the form of fractions or mixed numbers, e.g., by using visual fraction models or equations to represent the problem.	*125A–125B,* **125–128,** *503A–503B,* **503–506** See Also: *329A–329B,* 329–332
5.NF.B.4	Apply and extend previous understandings of multiplication to multiply a fraction or whole number by a fraction.	
	a. Interpret the product (a/b) $\times$ q as a parts of a partition of q into b equal parts; equivalently, as the result of a sequence of operations $a \times q + b$.	*421A–421B,* **421–424,** *427A–427B,* **427–430,** *433A–433B,* **433–436,** *439A–439B,* **439–442,** *451A–451B,* **451–454**
	b. Find the area of a rectangle with fractional side lengths by tiling it with unit squares of the appropriate unit fraction side lengths, and show that the area is the same as would be found by multiplying the side lengths. Multiply fractional side lengths to find areas of rectangles, and represent fraction products as rectangular areas.	*439A–439B,* **439–442,** *459A–459B,* **459–462,** *477A–477B,* **477–480**
5.NF.B.5	Interpret multiplication as scaling (resizing), by:	
	a. Comparing the size of a product to the size of one factor on the basis of the size of the other factor, without performing the indicated multiplication.	*445A–445B,* **445–448,** *465A–465B,* **465–468** See Also: *451A–451B,* 451–454
	b. Explaining why multiplying a given number by a fraction greater than 1 results in a product greater than the given number (recognizing multiplication by whole numbers greater than 1 as a familiar case); explaining why multiplying a given number by a fraction less than 1 results in a product smaller than the given number; and relating the principle of fraction equivalence $a/b = (n \times a)/(n \times b)$ to the effect of multiplying a/b by 1.	*445A–445B,* **445–448,** *451A–451B,* **451–454,** *465A–465B,* **465–468**
5.NF.B.6	Solve real world problems involving multiplication of fractions and mixed numbers, e.g., by using visual fraction models or equations to represent the problem.	*471A–471B,* **471–474,** *477A–477B,* **477–480** See Also: *125A–125B,* 125–128
5.NF.B.7	Apply and extend previous understandings of division to divide unit fractions by whole numbers and whole numbers by unit fractions.	
	a. Interpret division of a unit fraction by a non-zero whole number, and compute such quotients.	*491A–491B,* **491–494,** *517A–517B,* **517–520** See Also: *511A–511B,* 511–514
	b. Interpret division of a whole number by a unit fraction, and compute such quotients.	*491A–491B,* **491–494,** *497A–497B,* **497–500,** *517A–517B,* **517–520** See Also: *511A–511B,* 511–514
	c. Solve real world problems involving division of unit fractions by non-zero whole numbers and division of whole numbers by unit fractions, e.g., by using visual fraction models and equations to represent the problem.	*511A–511B,* **511–514** See Also: *491A–491B,* 491–494, *517A–517B,* 517–520

Pages only in Teacher Edition are shown in italics.

☐ **Cluster A: Convert like measurement units within a given measurement system.**

| 5.MD.A.1 | Convert among different-sized standard measurement units within a given measurement system (e.g., convert 5 cm to 0.05 m), and use these conversions in solving multi-step, real world problems. | *585A–585B*, *585–588*, *591A–591B*, *591–594*, *597A–597B*, *597–600*, *603A–603B*, *603–606*, *611A–611B*, *611–614*, *617A–617B*, *617–620*, *623A–623B*, *623–626* |

☐ **Cluster B: Represent and interpret data.**

| 5.MD.B.2 | Make a line plot to display a data set of measurements in fractions of a unit (1/2, 1/4, 1/8). Use operations on fractions for this grade to solve problems involving information presented in line plots. | *533A–533B*, *533–536* |

■ **Cluster C: Geometric measurement: understand concepts of volume.**

5.MD.C.3	Recognize volume as an attribute of solid figures and understand concepts of volume measurement.	*655A–655B*, *655–658*
	a. A cube with side length 1 unit, called a "unit cube," is said to have "one cubic unit" of volume, and can be used to measure volume.	*663A–663B*, *663–666*
	b. A solid figure which can be packed without gaps or overlaps using *n* unit cubes is said to have a volume of *n* cubic units.	*669A–669B*, *669–672* See Also: *675A–675B*, *675–678*
5.MD.C.4	Measure volumes by counting unit cubes, using cubic cm, cubic in, cubic ft, and improvised units.	*669A–669B*, *669–672*, *675A–675B*, *675–678*
5.MD.C.5	Relate volume to the operations of multiplication and addition and solve real world and mathematical problems involving volume.	
	a. Find the volume of a right rectangular prism with whole-number side lengths by packing it with unit cubes, and show that the volume is the same as would be found by multiplying the edge lengths, equivalently by multiplying the height by the area of the base. Represent threefold whole-number products as volumes, e.g., to represent the associative property of multiplication.	*681A–681B*, *681–684*, *687A–687B*, *687–690*
	b. Apply the formulas $V = l \times w \times h$ and $V = b \times h$ for rectangular prisms to find volumes of right rectangular prisms with whole-number edge lengths in the context of solving real world and mathematical problems.	*681A–681B*, *681–684*, *687A–687B*, *687–690*, *693A–693B*, *693–696* See Also: *699A–699B*, *699–702*
	c. Recognize volume as additive. Find volumes of solid figures composed of two non-overlapping right rectangular prisms by adding the volumes of the non-overlapping parts, applying this technique to solve real world problems.	*699A–699B*, *699–702*

Domain: Geometry

Cluster A: Graph points on the coordinate plane to solve real-world and mathematical problems.

5.G.A.1	Use a pair of perpendicular number lines, called axes, to define a coordinate system, with the intersection of the lines (the origin) arranged to coincide with the 0 on each line and a given point in the plane located by using an ordered pair of numbers, called its coordinates. Understand that the first number indicates how far to travel from the origin in the direction of one axis, and the second number indicates how far to travel in the direction of the second axis, with the convention that the names of the two axes and the coordinates correspond (e.g., *x*-axis and *x*-coordinate, *y*-axis and *y*-coordinate).	*539A–539B*, 539–542
5.G.A.2	Represent real world and mathematical problems by graphing points in the first quadrant of the coordinate plane, and interpret coordinate values of points in the context of the situation.	*545A–545B*, 545–548, *551A–551B*, 551–554

Cluster B: Classify two-dimensional figures into categories based on their properties.

5.G.B.3	Understand that attributes belonging to a category of two-dimensional figures also belong to all subcategories of that category. For example, all rectangles have four right angles and squares are rectangles, so all squares have four right angles.	*637A–637B*, 637–640, *643A–643B*, 643–646, *649A–649B*, 649–652
5.G.B.4	Classify two-dimensional figures in a hierarchy based on properties.	*637A–637B*, 637–640, *643A–643B*, 643–646, *649A–649B*, 649–652

Pages only in Teacher Edition are shown in italics.

Student Edition Glossary

Glossary

Pronunciation Key

a	add, map	ē	equal, tree	m	move, seem	o͞o	pool, food	u̇	pull, book
ā	ace, rate	f	fit, half	n	nice, tin	p	pit, stop	û(r)	burn, term
â(r)	care, air	g	go, log	ng	ring, song	r	run, poor	yo͞o	fuse, few
ä	palm, father	h	hope, hate	o	odd, hot	s	see, pass	v	vain, eve
b	bat, rub	i	it, give	ō	open, so	sh	sure, rush	w	win, away
ch	check, catch	ī	ice, write	ô	order, jaw	t	talk, sit	y	yet, yearn
d	dog, rod	j	joy, ledge	oi	oil, boy	th	thin, both	z	zest, muse
e	end, pet	k	cool, take	ou	pout, now	th	this, bathe	zh	vision, pleasure
		l	look, rule	o͝o	took, full	u	up, done		

ə the schwa, an unstressed vowel representing the sound spelled a in above, e in sicken, i in possible, o in melon, u in circus

Other symbols:
- • separates words into syllables
- ′ indicates stress on a syllable

A

acute angle [ə•kyo͞ot′ ang′gəl] **ángulo agudo** An angle that has a measure less than a right angle (less than 90° and greater than 0°)
Example:

Word History

The Latin word for needle is *acus*. This means "pointed" or "sharp." You will recognize the root in the words *acid* (sharp taste), *acumen* (mental sharpness), and acute, which describes a sharp or pointed angle.

acute triangle [ə•kyo͞ot′ trī′ang•gəl] **triángulo acutángulo** A triangle that has three acute angles

addend [ad′end] **sumando** A number that is added to another in an addition problem

addition [ə•dish′ən] **suma** The process of finding the total number of items when two or more groups of items are joined; the inverse operation of subtraction

algebraic expression [al•jə•brā′ik ek•spresh′ən] **expresión algebraica** An expression that includes at least one variable
Examples: $x + 5$, $3a - 4$

angle [ang′gəl] **ángulo** A shape formed by two rays that share the same endpoint
Example:

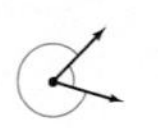

area [âr′ē•ə] **área** The measure of the number of unit squares needed to cover a surface

array [ə•rā′] **matriz** An arrangement of objects in rows and columns
Example:

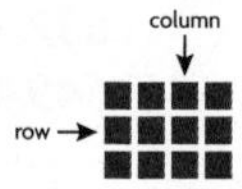
column
row

Associative Property of Addition [ə•sō′shē•āt•iv präp′ ər•tē əv ə•dish′ən] **propiedad asociativa de la suma** The property that states that when the grouping of addends is changed, the sum is the same
Example: $(5 + 8) + 4 = 5 + (8 + 4)$

Associative Property of Multiplication [ə•sō′shē•āt•iv präp′ər•tē əv mul•tə•pli•kā′shən] **propiedad asociativa de la multiplicación** The property that states that factors can be grouped in different ways and still get the same product
Example: $(2 \times 3) \times 4 = 2 \times (3 \times 4)$

B

balance [bal′əns] **equilibrar** To equalize in weight or number

bar graph [bär graf] **gráfica de barras** A graph that uses horizontal or vertical bars to display countable data
Example:

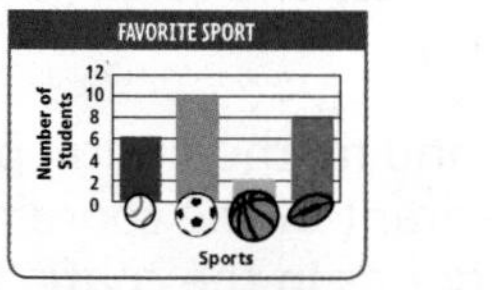
FAVORITE SPORT
Number of Students
12
10
8
6
4
2
0
Sports

base (arithmetic) [bās] **base** A number used as a repeated factor
Example: $8^3 = 8 \times 8 \times 8$. The base is 8.

base (geometry) [bās] **base** In two dimensions, one side of a triangle or parallelogram that is used to help find the area. In three dimensions, a plane figure, usually a polygon or circle, by which a three-dimensional figure is measured or named
Examples:

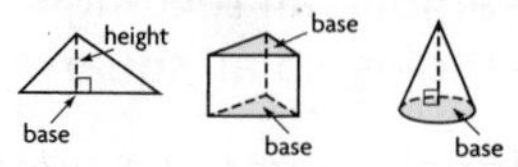
height
base
base
base
base

benchmark [bench′märk] **punto de referencia** A familiar number used as a point of reference

C

capacity [kə•pas′i•tē] **capacidad** The amount a container can hold when filled

Celsius (°C) [sel′sē•əs] **Celsius (°C)** A metric scale for measuring temperature

centimeter (cm) [sen′tə•mēt•ər] **centímetro (cm)** A metric unit used to measure length or distance; 0.01 meter = 1 centimeter

closed figure [klōzd fig′yər] **figura cerrada** A figure that begins and ends at the same point

common denominator [käm′ən dē•näm′ə•nāt•ər] **denominador común** A common multiple of two or more denominators
Example: Some common denominators for $\frac{1}{4}$ and $\frac{5}{6}$ are 12, 24, and 36.

common factor [käm′ən fak′tər] **factor común** A number that is a factor of two or more numbers

common multiple [käm′ən mul′tə•pəl] **múltiplo común** A number that is a multiple of two or more numbers

Commutative Property of Addition [kə•myo͞ot′ə•tiv präp′ər•tē əv ə•dish′ən] **propiedad conmutativa de la suma** The property that states that when the order of two addends is changed, the sum is the same
Example: $4 + 5 = 5 + 4$

Commutative Property of Multiplication [kə•myo͞ot′ə•tiv präp′ər•tē əv mul•tə•pli•kā′shən] **propiedad conmutativa de la multiplicación** The property that states that when the order of two factors is changed, the product is the same
Example: $4 \times 5 = 5 \times 4$

compatible numbers [kəm•pat′ə•bəl num′bərz] **números compatibles** Numbers that are easy to compute with mentally

composite number [kəm•päz′it num′bər] **número compuesto** A number having more than two factors
Example: 6 is a composite number, since its factors are 1, 2, 3, and 6.

cone [kōn] **cono** A solid figure that has a flat, circular base and one vertex
Example:

congruent [kən•gro͞o′ənt] **congruente** Having the same size and shape

coordinate grid [kō•ôrd′n•it grid] **cuadrícula de coordenadas** A grid formed by a horizontal line called the *x*-axis and a vertical line called the *y*-axis
Example:

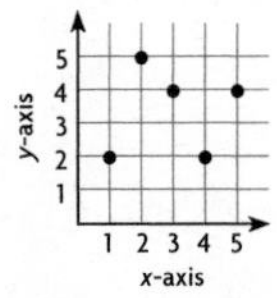
y-axis
5
4
3
2
1
1 2 3 4 5
x-axis

counting number [kount′ing num′bər] **número natural** A whole number that can be used to count a set of objects (1, 2, 3, 4, . . .)

cube [kyo͞ob] **cubo** A three-dimensional figure with six congruent square faces
Example:

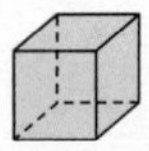

cubic unit [kyo͞o′bik yo͞o′nit] **unidad cúbica** A unit used to measure volume such as cubic foot (ft^3), cubic meter (m^3), and so on

cup (c) [kup] **taza (t)** A customary unit used to measure capacity; 8 ounces = 1 cup

cylinder [sil′ən•dər] **cilindro** A solid figure that has two parallel bases that are congruent circles
Example:

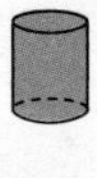

D

data [dāt′ə] **datos** Information collected about people or things, often to draw conclusions about them

decagon [dek′ə•gän] **decágono** A polygon with ten sides and ten angles
Examples:

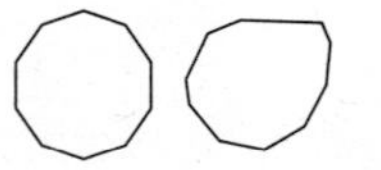

decagonal prism [dek•ag′ə•nəl priz′əm] **prisma decagonal** A three-dimensional figure with two decagonal bases and ten rectangular faces

decimal [des′ə•məl] **decimal** A number with one or more digits to the right of the decimal point

decimal point [des′ə•məl point] **punto decimal** A symbol used to separate dollars from cents in money, and to separate the ones place from the tenths place in a decimal

decimal system [des′ə•məl sis′təm] **sistema decimal** A system of computation based on the number 10

decimeter (dm) [des′i•mēt•ər] **decímetro (dm)** A metric unit used to measure length or distance; 10 decimeters = 1 meter

degree (°) [di•grē′] **grado (°)** A unit used for measuring angles and temperature

degree Celsius (°C) [di•grē′ sel′sē•əs] **grado Celsius** A metric unit for measuring temperature

degree Fahrenheit (°F) [di•grē′ fâr′ən•hīt′] **grado Fahrenheit** A customary unit for measuring temperature

dekameter (dam) [dek′ə•mēt•ər] **decámetro** A metric unit used to measure length or distance; 10 meters = 1 dekameter

denominator [dē•näm′ə•nāt•ər] **denominador** The number below the bar in a fraction that tells how many equal parts are in the whole or in the group
Example: $\frac{3}{4}$ ← denominator

diagonal [dī•ag′ə•nəl] **diagonal** A line segment that connects two non-adjacent vertices of a polygon
Example:

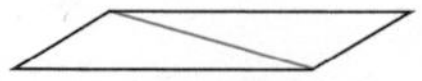

difference [dif′ər•əns] **diferencia** The answer to a subtraction problem

digit [dij′it] **dígito** Any one of the ten symbols 0, 1, 2, 3, 4, 5, 6, 7, 8, 9 used to write numbers

dimension [də•men′shən] **dimensión** A measure in one direction

Distributive Property [di•strib′yo͞o•tiv präp′ər•tē] **propiedad distributiva** The property that states that multiplying a sum by a number is the same as multiplying each addend in the sum by the number and then adding the products
Example: $3 \times (4 + 2) = (3 \times 4) + (3 \times 2)$
$3 \times 6 = 12 + 6$
$18 = 18$

divide [də•vīd′] **dividir** To separate into equal groups; the inverse operation of multiplication

dividend [div′ə•dend] **dividendo** The number that is to be divided in a division problem
Example: $36 \div 6$; $6\overline{)36}$ The dividend is 36.

division [də•vizh′ən] **división** The process of sharing a number of items to find how many equal groups can be made or how many items will be in each equal group; the inverse operation of multiplication

divisor [də•vī′zər] **divisor** The number that divides the dividend
Example: $15 \div 3$; $3\overline{)15}$ The divisor is 3.

E

edge [ej] **arista** The line segment made where two faces of a solid figure meet
Example:

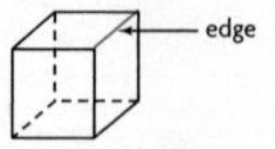
edge

elapsed time [ē•lapst′ tīm] **tiempo transcurrido** The time that passes between the start of an activity and the end of that activity

endpoint [end′ point] **extremo** The point at either end of a line segment or the starting point of a ray

equal to (=) [ē′kwəl to͞o] **igual a** Having the same value

equation [ē•kwā′zhən] **ecuación** An algebraic or numerical sentence that shows that two quantities are equal

equilateral triangle [ē•kwi•lat′ər•əl trī′ang•gəl] **triángulo equilátero** A triangle with three congruent sides
Example:

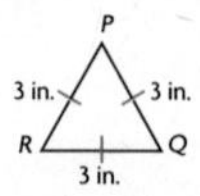
P
3 in.
3 in.
R
Q
3 in.

equivalent [ē•kwiv′ə•lənt] **equivalente** Having the same value

equivalent decimals [ē•kwiv′ə•lənt des′ə•məlz] **decimales equivalentes** Decimals that name the same amount
Example: 0.4 = 0.40 = 0.400

equivalent fractions [ē•kwiv′ə•lənt frak′shənz] **fracciones equivalentes** Fractions that name the same amount or part
Example: $\frac{3}{4} = \frac{6}{8}$

estimate [es′tə•mit] *noun* **estimación (s)** A number close to an exact amount

estimate [es′tə•māt] *verb* **estimar (v)** To find a number that is close to an exact amount

evaluate [ē•val′yo͞o•āt] **evaluar** To find the value of a numerical or algebraic expression

even [ē′vən] **par** A whole number that has a 0, 2, 4, 6, or 8 in the ones place

expanded form [ek•span′did fôrm] **forma desarrollada** A way to write numbers by showing the value of each digit
Examples: $832 = 8 \times 100 + 3 \times 10 + 2 \times 1$
$3.25 = (3 \times 1) + (2 \times \frac{1}{10}) + (5 \times \frac{1}{100})$

exponent [eks'•pōn•ənt] **exponente** A number that shows how many times the base is used as a factor
Example: $10^3 = 10 \times 10 \times 10$.
3 is the exponent.

expression [ek•spresh'ən] **expresión** A mathematical phrase or the part of a number sentence that combines numbers, operation signs, and sometimes variables, but does not have an equal sign

F

face [fās] **cara** A polygon that is a flat surface of a solid figure
Example:

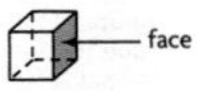
face

fact family [fakt fam'ə•lē] **familia de operaciones** A set of related multiplication and division, or addition and subtraction, equations
Examples: $7 \times 8 = 56$; $8 \times 7 = 56$; $56 \div 7 = 8$; $56 \div 8 = 7$

factor [fak'tər] **factor** A number multiplied by another number to find a product

Fahrenheit (°F) [fâr'ən•hīt] **Fahrenheit (°F)** A customary scale for measuring temperature

fluid ounce (fl oz) [flōō'id ouns] **onza fluida** A customary unit used to measure liquid capacity; 1 cup = 8 fluid ounces

foot (ft) [fōōt] **pie (ft)** A customary unit used to measure length or distance; 1 foot = 12 inches

formula [fôr'myōō•lə] **fórmula** A set of symbols that expresses a mathematical rule
Example: $A = b \times h$

fraction [frak'shən] **fracción** A number that names a part of a whole or a part of a group

fraction greater than 1 [frak'shən grāt'ər than wun] **fracción mayor que 1** A number which has a numerator that is greater than its denominator
Example:

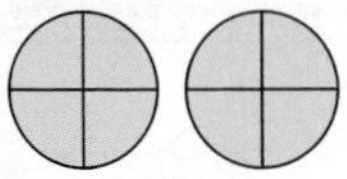

$\frac{8}{4}$

G

gallon (gal) [gal'ən] **galón (gal)** A customary unit used to measure capacity; 4 quarts = 1 gallon

general quadrilateral [jen'ər•əl kwä•dri•lat'ər•əl] **cuadrilátero en general** See *quadrilateral.*

gram (g) [gram] **gramo (g)** A metric unit used to measure mass; 1,000 grams = 1 kilogram

greater than (>) [grāt'ər than] **mayor que (>)** A symbol used to compare two numbers or two quantities when the greater number or greater quantity is given first
Example: $6 > 4$

greater than or equal to (≥) [grāt'ər than ôr ē'kwəl tōō] **mayor que o igual a** A symbol used to compare two numbers or quantities when the first is greater than or equal to the second

greatest common factor [grāt'əst käm'ən fak'tər] **máximo común divisor** The greatest factor that two or more numbers have in common
Example: 6 is the greatest common factor of 18 and 30.

grid [grid] **cuadrícula** Evenly divided and equally spaced squares on a figure or flat surface

H

height [hīt] **altura** The length of a perpendicular from the base to the top of a two-dimensional or three-dimensional figure
Example:

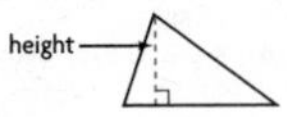
height

heptagon [hep'tə•gän] **heptágono** A polygon with seven sides and seven angles

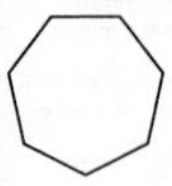

hexagon [hek'sə•gän] **hexágono** A polygon with six sides and six angles
Examples:

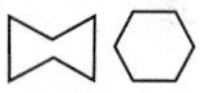

hexagonal prism [hek•sag'ə•nəl priz'əm] **prisma hexagonal** A three-dimensional figure with two hexagonal bases and six rectangular faces

horizontal [hôr•i•zänt'l] **horizontal** Extending left and right

hundredth [hun'dredth] **centésimo** One of 100 equal parts
Examples: 0.56, $\frac{56}{100}$, fifty-six hundredths

I

Identity Property of Addition [ī•den'tə•tē präp'ər•tē əv ə•dish'ən] **propiedad de identidad de la suma** The property that states that when you add zero to a number, the result is that number

Identity Property of Multiplication [ī•den'tə•tē präp'ər•tē əv mul•tə•pli•kā'shən] **propiedad de identidad de la multiplicación** The property that states that the product of any number and 1 is that number

inch (in.) [inch] **pulgada (pulg)** A customary unit used to measure length or distance; 12 inches = 1 foot

inequality [in•ē•kwôl'ə•tē] **desigualdad** A mathematical sentence that contains the symbol $<$, $>$, $\leq$, $\geq$, or $\neq$

intersecting lines [in•tər•sekt'ing līnz] **líneas secantes** Lines that cross each other at exactly one point
Example:

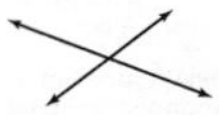

interval [in'tər•vəl] **intervalo** The difference between one number and the next on the scale of a graph

inverse operations [in'vûrs äp•ə•rā'shənz] **operaciones inversas** Opposite operations, or operations that undo each other, such as addition and subtraction or multiplication and division

isosceles triangle [ī•säs'ə•lēz trī'ang•gəl] **triángulo isósceles** A triangle with two congruent sides
Example:

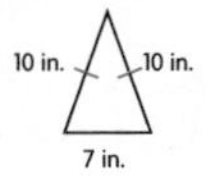
10 in.
10 in.
7 in.

K

key [kē] **clave** The part of a map or graph that explains the symbols

kilogram (kg) [kil'ō•gram] **kilogramo (kg)** A metric unit used to measure mass; 1,000 grams = 1 kilogram

kilometer (km) [kə•läm'ət•ər] **kilómetro (km)** A metric unit used to measure length or distance; 1,000 meters = 1 kilometer

L

lateral face [lat'ər•əl fās] **cara lateral** Any surface of a polyhedron other than a base

least common denominator [lēst käm'ən dē•näm'ə•nāt•ər] **mínimo común denominador** The least common multiple of two or more denominators
Example: The least common denominator for $\frac{1}{4}$ and $\frac{5}{6}$ is 12.

least common multiple [lēst käm'ən mul'tə•pəl] **mínimo común múltiplo** The least number that is a common multiple of two or more numbers

less than (<) [les than] **menor que (<)** A symbol used to compare two numbers or two quantities, with the lesser number given first
Example: $4 < 6$

less than or equal to (≤) [les than ôr ē'kwəl tōō] **menor que o igual a** A symbol used to compare two numbers or two quantities, when the first is less than or equal to the second

line [līn] **línea** A straight path in a plane, extending in both directions with no endpoints
Example:

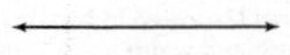

line graph [līn graf] **gráfica lineal** A graph that uses line segments to show how data change over time

line plot [līn plät] **diagrama de puntos** A graph that shows frequency of data along a number line
Example:

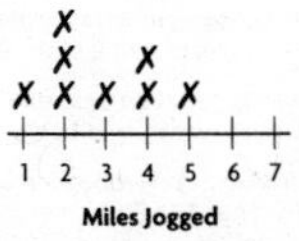
1 2 3 4 5 6 7
Miles Jogged

line segment [līn seg'mənt] **segmento** A part of a line that includes two points called endpoints and all the points between them

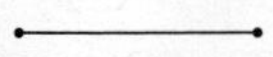

line symmetry [līn sim'ə•trē] **simetría axial** A figure has line symmetry if it can be folded about a line so that its two parts match exactly.

linear unit [lin'ē•ər yōō'nit] **unidad lineal** A measure of length, width, height, or distance

liquid volume [lik'wid väl'yōōm] **volumen de un líquido** The amount of liquid in a container

liter (L) [lēt'ər] **litro (L)** A metric unit used to measure capacity; 1 liter = 1,000 milliliters

M

mass [mas] **masa** The amount of matter in an object

meter (m) [mēt'ər] **metro (m)** A metric unit used to measure length or distance; 1 meter = 100 centimeters

mile (mi) [mīl] **milla (mi)** A customary unit used to measure length or distance; 5,280 feet = 1 mile

milligram (mg) [mil'i•gram] **miligramo** A metric unit used to measure mass; 1,000 milligrams = 1 gram

milliliter (mL) [mil'i•lēt•ər] **mililitro (mL)** A metric unit used to measure capacity; 1,000 milliliters = 1 liter

millimeter (mm) [mil'i•mēt•ər] **milímetro (mm)** A metric unit used to measure length or distance; 1,000 millimeters = 1 meter

million [mil'yən] **millón** 1,000 thousands; written as 1,000,000

mixed number [mikst num'bər] **número mixto** A number that is made up of a whole number and a fraction
Example: $1\frac{5}{8}$

multiple [mul'tə•pəl] **múltiplo** The product of two counting numbers is a multiple of each of those numbers

multiplication [mul•tə•pli•kā'shən] **multiplicación** A process to find the total number of items made up of equal-sized groups, or to find the total number of items in a given number of groups. It is the inverse operation of division.

multiply [mul'tə•plī] **multiplicar** When you combine equal groups, you can multiply to find how many in all; the inverse operation of division

N

nonagon [nän'ə•gän] **eneágono** A polygon with nine sides and nine angles

not equal to (≠) [not ē'kwəl tōō] **no igual a** A symbol that indicates one quantity is not equal to another

number line [num'bər līn] **recta numérica** A line on which numbers can be located
Example:

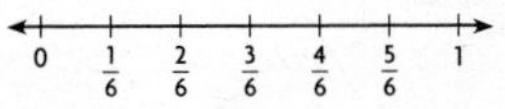
0
1/6
2/6
3/6
4/6
5/6
1

numerator [nōō'mər•āt•ər] **numerador** The number above the bar in a fraction that tells how many equal parts of the whole or group are being considered
Example: $\frac{3}{4}$ ← numerator

numerical expression [nōō•mer'i•kəl ek•spresh'ən] **expresión numérica** A mathematical phrase that uses only numbers and operation signs

O

obtuse angle [äb•tōōs' ang'gəl] **ángulo obtuso** An angle whose measure is greater than 90° and less than 180°
Example:

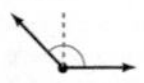

obtuse triangle [äb•tōōs' trī'ang•gəl] **triángulo obtusángulo** A triangle that has one obtuse angle

octagon [äk'tə•gän] **octágono** A polygon with eight sides and eight angles
Examples:

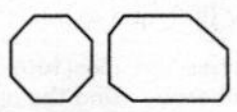

octagonal prism [äk•tag'ə•nəl priz'əm] **prisma octagonal** A three-dimensional figure with two octagonal bases and eight rectangular faces

odd [od] **impar** A whole number that has a 1, 3, 5, 7, or 9 in the ones place

open figure [ō'pən fig'yər] **figura abierta** A figure that does not begin and end at the same point

order of operations [ôr'dər əv äp•ə•rā'shənz] **orden de las operaciones** A special set of rules which gives the order in which calculations are done in an expression

ordered pair [ôr'dərd pâr] **par ordenado** A pair of numbers used to locate a point on a grid. The first number tells the left-right position and the second number tells the up-down position

origin [ôr'ə•jin] **origen** The point where the two axes of a coordinate grid intersect; (0, 0)

ounce (oz) [ouns] **onza (oz)** A customary unit used to measure weight; 16 ounces = 1 pound

overestimate [ō'vər•es•tə•mit] **sobrestimar** An estimate that is greater than the exact answer

P

pan balance [pan bal'əns] **balanza de platillos** An instrument used to weigh objects and to compare the weights of objects

parallel lines [pâr'ə•lel līnz] **líneas paralelas** Lines in the same plane that never intersect and are always the same distance apart
Example:

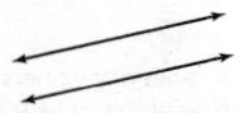

parallelogram [pâr•ə•lel'ə•gram] **paralelogramo** A quadrilateral whose opposite sides are parallel and have the same length, or are congruent
Example:

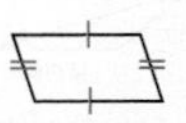

parentheses [pə•ren'thə•sēz] **paréntesis** The symbols used to show which operation or operations in an expression should be done first

partial product [pär'shəl präd'əkt] **producto parcial** A method of multiplying in which the ones, tens, hundreds, and so on are multiplied separately and then the products are added together

partial quotient [pär'shəl kwō'shənt] **cociente parcial** A method of dividing in which multiples of the divisor are subtracted from the dividend and then the quotients are added together

Student Edition Glossary continued

pattern [pat'ərn] **patrón** An ordered set of numbers or objects; the order helps you predict what will come next
Examples: 2, 4, 6, 8, 10

pentagon [pen'tə•gän] **pentágono** A polygon with five sides and five angles
Examples:

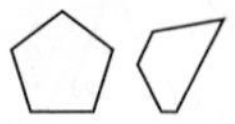

pentagonal prism [pen•tag'ə•nəl priz'əm] **prisma pentagonal** A three-dimensional figure with two pentagonal bases and five rectangular faces

pentagonal pyramid [pen•tag'ə•nəl pir'ə•mid] **pirámide pentagonal** A pyramid with a pentagonal base and five triangular faces

perimeter [pə•rim'ə•tər] **perímetro** The distance around a closed plane figure

period [pir'ē•əd] **período** Each group of three digits separated by commas in a multi-digit number
Example: 85,643,900 has three periods.

perpendicular lines [pər•pən•dik'yōō•lər līnz] **líneas perpendiculares** Two lines that intersect to form four right angles
Example:

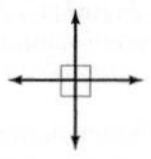

picture graph [pik'chər graf] **gráfica con dibujos** A graph that displays countable data with symbols or pictures
Example:

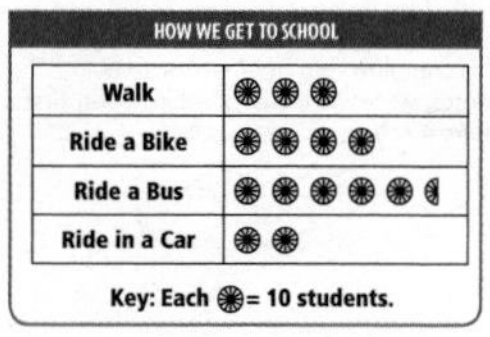
HOW WE GET TO SCHOOL
Walk
Ride a Bike
Ride a Bus
Ride in a Car
Key: Each = 10 students.

pint (pt) [pīnt] **pinta** A customary unit used to measure capacity; 2 cups = 1 pint

place value [plās val'yōō] **valor posicional** The value of each digit in a number based on the location of the digit

plane [plān] **plano** A flat surface that extends without end in all directions
Example:

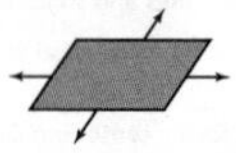

plane figure [plān fig'yər] **figura plana** See *two-dimensional figure*

point [point] **punto** An exact location in space

polygon [päl'i•gän] **polígono** A closed plane figure formed by three or more line segments
Examples:

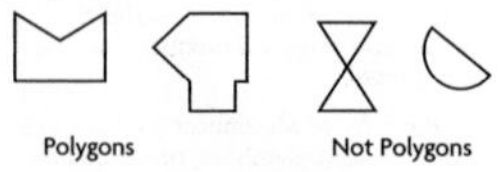
Polygons
Not Polygons

polyhedron [päl•i•hē'drən] **poliedro** A solid figure with faces that are polygons
Examples:

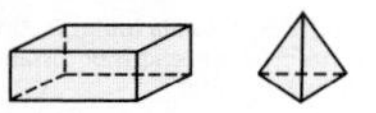

pound (lb) [pound] **libra (lb)** A customary unit used to measure weight;
1 pound = 16 ounces

prime number [prīm num'bər] **número primo** A number that has exactly two factors: 1 and itself
Examples: 2, 3, 5, 7, 11, 13, 17, and 19 are prime numbers. 1 is not a prime number.

prism [priz'əm] **prisma** A solid figure that has two congruent, polygon-shaped bases, and other faces that are all rectangles
Examples:

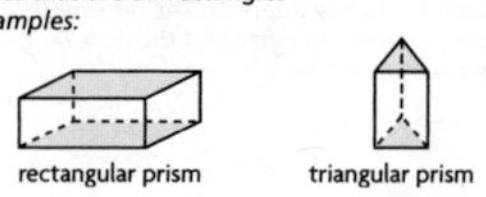
rectangular prism
triangular prism

product [präd'əkt] **producto** The answer to a multiplication problem

protractor [prō'trak•tər] **transportador** A tool used for measuring or drawing angles

pyramid [pir'ə•mid] **pirámide** A solid figure with a polygon base and all other faces are triangles that meet at a common vertex
Example:

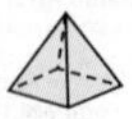

Word History

A fire is sometimes in the shape of a pyramid, with a point at the top and a wider base. This may be how *pyramid* got its name. The Greek word for fire was *pura*, which may have been combined with the Egyptian word for pyramid, *pimar*.

Q

quadrilateral [kwä•dri•lat'ər•əl] **cuadrilátero** A polygon with four sides and four angles
Example:

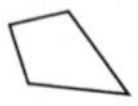

quart (qt) [kwôrt] **cuarto (ct)** A customary unit used to measure capacity; 2 pints = 1 quart

quotient [kwō'shənt] **cociente** The number that results from dividing
Example: 8 ÷ 4 = 2. The quotient is 2.

R

range [rānj] **rango** The difference between the greatest and least numbers in a data set

ray [rā] **semirrecta** A part of a line; it has one endpoint and continues without end in one direction
Example:

rectangle [rek'tang•gəl] **rectángulo** A parallelogram with four right angles
Example:

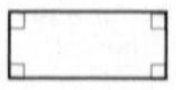

rectangular prism [rek•tang'gyə•lər priz'əm] **prisma rectangular** A three-dimensional figure in which all six faces are rectangles
Example:

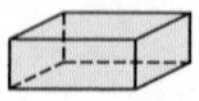

rectangular pyramid [rek•tang'gyə•lər pir'ə•mid] **pirámide rectangular** A pyramid with a rectangular base and four triangular faces

regroup [rē•grōōp'] **reagrupar** To exchange amounts of equal value to rename a number
Example: 5 + 8 = 13 ones or 1 ten 3 ones

regular polygon [reg'yə•lər päl'i•gän] **polígono regular** A polygon in which all sides are congruent and all angles are congruent

related facts [ri•lāt'id fakts] **operaciones relacionadas** A set of related addition and subtraction, or multiplication and division, number sentences
Examples: 4 × 7 = 28   28 ÷ 4 = 7
7 × 4 = 28   28 ÷ 7 = 4

remainder [ri•mān'dər] **residuo** The amount left over when a number cannot be divided equally

rhombus [räm'bəs] **rombo** A parallelogram with four equal, or congruent, sides
Example:

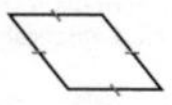

Word History

Rhombus is almost identical to its Greek origin, *rhombos*. The original meaning was "spinning top" or "magic wheel," which is easy to imagine when you look at a rhombus, an equilateral parallelogram.

right angle [rīt ang'gəl] **ángulo recto** An angle that forms a square corner and has a measure of 90°
Example:

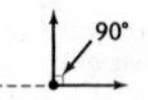
90°

right triangle [rīt trī'ang•gəl] **triángulo rectángulo** A triangle that has a right angle
Example:

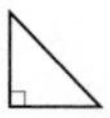

round [round] **redondear** To replace a number with one that is simpler and is approximately the same size as the original number
Example: 114.6 rounded to the nearest ten is 110 and to the nearest one is 115.

S

scale [skāl] **escala** A series of numbers placed at fixed distances on a graph to help label the graph

scalene triangle [skā'lēn trī'ang•gəl] **triángulo escaleno** A triangle with no congruent sides
Example:

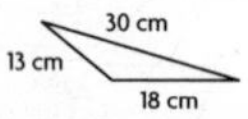
30 cm
13 cm
18 cm

second (sec) [sek'ənd] **segundo (seg)** A small unit of time; 60 seconds = 1 minute

sequence [sē'kwəns] **sucesión** An ordered list of numbers

simplest form [sim'pləst fôrm] **mínima expresión** A fraction is in simplest form when the numerator and denominator have only 1 as a common factor.

skip count [skip kount] **contar salteado** A pattern of counting forward or backward
Example: 5, 10, 15, 20, 25, 30, . . .

solid figure [sä'lid fig'yər] **cuerpo geométrico** See *three-dimensional figure*

solution [sə•lōō'shən] **solución** A value that, when substituted for the variable, makes an equation true

sphere [sfir] **esfera** A solid figure whose curved surface is the same distance from the center to all its points
Example:

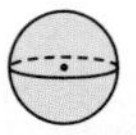

square [skwâr] **cuadrado** A polygon with four equal, or congruent, sides and four right angles

square pyramid [skwâr pir'ə•mid] **pirámide cuadrada** A solid figure with a square base and with four triangular faces that have a common vertex
Example:

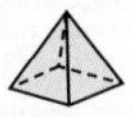

square unit [skwâr yōō'nit] **unidad cuadrada** A unit used to measure area such as square foot (ft^2), square meter (m^2), and so on

standard form [stan'dərd fôrm] **forma normal** A way to write numbers by using the digits 0–9, with each digit having a place value
Example: 456 ← standard form

straight angle [strāt ang'gəl] **ángulo llano** An angle whose measure is 180°
Example:

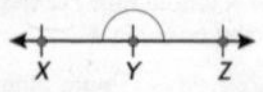
X
Y
Z

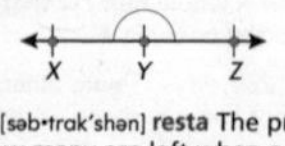

subtraction [səb•trak'shən] **resta** The process of finding how many are left when a number of items are taken away from a group of items; the process of finding the difference when two groups are compared; the inverse operation of addition

sum [sum] **suma o total** The answer to an addition problem

T

tablespoon (tbsp) [tā'bəl•spōōn] **cucharada (cda)** A customary unit used to measure capacity; 3 teaspoons = 1 tablespoon

tally table [tal'ē tā'bəl] **tabla de conteo** A table that uses tally marks to record data

teaspoon (tsp) [tē'spōōn] **cucharadita (cdta)** A customary unit used to measure capacity; 1 tablespoon = 3 teaspoons

tenth [tenth] **décimo** One of ten equal parts
Example: 0.7 = seven tenths

term [tûrm] **término** A number in a sequence

thousandth [thou'zəndth] **milésimo** One of one thousand equal parts
Example: 0.006 = six thousandths

three-dimensional [thrē də•men'shə•nəl] **tridimensional** Measured in three directions, such as length, width, and height

three-dimensional figure [thrē də•men'shə•nəl fig'yər] **figura tridimensional** A figure having length, width, and height
Example:

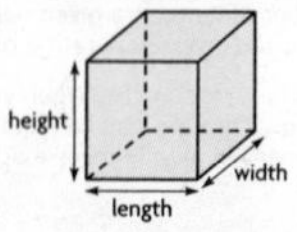
height
width
length

ton (T) [tun] **tonelada** A customary unit used to measure weight; 2,000 pounds = 1 ton

trapezoid [trap'i•zoid] **trapecio** A quadrilateral with at least one pair of parallel sides
Examples:

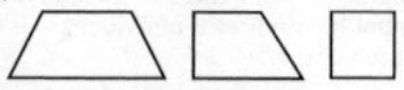

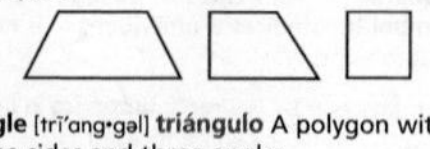

triangle [trī'ang•gəl] **triángulo** A polygon with three sides and three angles
Examples:

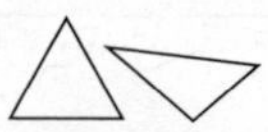

triangular prism [trī•ang'gyə•lər priz'əm] **prisma triangular** A solid figure that has two triangular bases and three rectangular faces

triangular pyramid [trī•ang'gyə•lər pir'ə•mid] **pirámide triangular** A pyramid that has a triangular base and three triangular faces

two-dimensional [tōō də•men'shə•nəl] **bidimensional** Measured in two directions, such as length and width

two-dimensional figure [tōō də•men'shə•nəl fig'yər] **figura bidimensional** A figure that lies in a plane; a figure having length and width

U

underestimate [un•dər•es'tə•mit] **subestimar** An estimate that is less than the exact answer

unit cube [yōō'nit kyōōb] **cubo unitario** A cube that has a length, width, and height of 1 unit

unit fraction [yōō'nit frak'shən] **fracción unitaria** A fraction that has 1 as a numerator

unit square [yōō'nit skwâr] **cuadrado de una unidad** A square with a side length of 1 unit, used to measure area

V

variable [vâr'ē•ə•bəl] **variable** A letter or symbol that stands for an unknown number or numbers

Venn diagram [ven dī'ə•gram] **diagrama de Venn** A diagram that shows relationships among sets of things
Example:

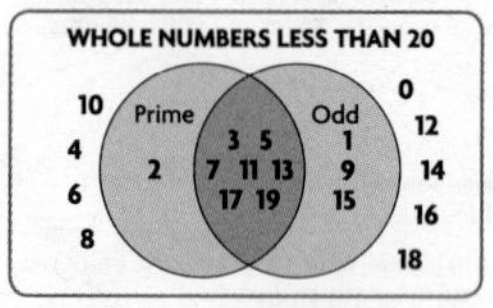
WHOLE NUMBERS LESS THAN 20
Prime
Odd
10
4
6
8
2
3 5
7 11 13
17 19
1
9
15
0
12
14
16
18

vertex [vûr′teks] vértice The point where two or more rays meet; the point of intersection of two sides of a polygon; the point of intersection of three (or more) edges of a solid figure; the top point of a cone; the plural of vertex is vertices
Examples:

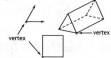

Word History

The Latin word *vertere* means "to turn" and also relates to "highest." You can turn a figure around a point, or *vertex*.

vertical [vûr′tĭ·kəl] vertical Extending up and down

volume [väl′yōōm] volumen The measure of the space a solid figure occupies

weight [wāt] peso How heavy an object is

whole [hōl] entero All of the parts of a shape or group

whole number [hōl num′bər] número entero One of the numbers 0, 1, 2, 3, 4, . . . ; the set of whole numbers goes on without end

word form [wûrd fôrm] en palabras A way to write numbers in standard English
Example: 4,829 = four thousand, eight hundred twenty-nine

x-axis [eks ak′sis] eje de la *x* The horizontal number line on a coordinate plane

x-coordinate [eks kō·ôrd′n·it] coordenada *x* The first number in an ordered pair; tells the distance to move right or left from (0, 0)

yard (yd) [yärd] yarda (yd) A customary unit used to measure length or distance; 3 feet = 1 yard

y-axis [wī ak′sis] eje de la *y* The vertical number line on a coordinate plane

y-coordinate [wī kō·ôrd′n·it] coordenada *y* The second number in an ordered pair; tells the distance to move up or down from (0, 0)

Zero Property of Multiplication [zē′rō präp′ər·tē əv mul·tə·pli·kā′shən] propiedad del cero de la multiplicación The property that states that when you multiply by zero, the product is zero

Professional Development References

Ashlock, R. (2010). Error patterns in computation: Using error patterns to help each student learn (10th ed.). Boston, MA: Allyn & Bacon.

Baldi, S., Jin, Y., Skemer, M., Green, P. J. & Herget, D. (2007). *Highlights from PISA 2006: Performance of U.S. 15-year-old students in science and mathematics literacy in an international context* (NCES-2008-016). National Center for Education Statistics, Institute of Education Sciences. Washington, DC: U.S. Department of Education.

Battista, M. T. (2007). The development of geometric and spatial thinking. In F. K. Lester (Ed.), *Second handbook of research on mathematics teaching and learning: Volume 2* (pp. 843–908). Charlotte, NC: Information Age Publishing.

Casa, T. M., & Gavin, M. K. (2009). Advancing students' understanding of quadrilaterals. In T. V. Craine & R. Rubenstein (Eds.), *Understanding geometry for a changing world* (pp. 205–220). Reston, VA: NCTM.

de Groot, C., & Whalen, T. (2006). Longing for division. *Teaching Children Mathematics, 12*(8), 410–418.

de Villiers, M., Govender, R., & Patterson, N. (2009). Defining in geometry. In T. V. Craine & R. Rubenstein (Eds.*), Understanding geometry for a changing world: Seventy-first yearbook* (pp. 189–203). Reston, VA: NCTM.

Flores, A. (2002). Profound understanding of division of fractions. In B. H. Litwiller (Ed.), Making sense of fractions, ratios, and proportions, 2002 Yearbook (p. 237–246). Reston, VA: NCTM

Furhman, S. H., Resnick, L., & Shepard, L. (2009). Standards aren't enough. *Education Week, 29*(7), 28.

Gonzales, P., Williams, T., Jocelyn, L., Roey, S., Katsberg, D., & Brenwald, S. (2008). *Highlights from TIMSS 2007: Mathematics and science achievement of U.S. fourth- and eighth-grade students in an international context* (NCES 2009–001 Revised). National Center for Education Statistics, Institute of Education Sciences. Washington, DC: U.S. Department of Education.

Heddens, J. W., & Speer, W. R. (2006). *Today's mathematics: Concepts, methods, and instructional activities* (11th ed.). Hoboken, NJ: John Wiley & Sons.

Irwin, K. C. (2001). Using everyday knowledge of decimals to enhance understanding. *Journal for Research in Mathematics Education, 32*(4), 399–420.

Kamii, C., & Warrington, M. A. (1999). Teaching fractions: Fostering children's own reasoning. In L. V. Stiff & F. R. Curcio (Eds.), *Developing mathematical reasoning in grades K-12: 1999 yearbook* (pp. 82–92). Reston, VA: National Council of Teachers of Mathematics.

Monk, S. (2003). Representation in school mathematics: Learning to graph and graphing to learn. In J. Kilpatrick, W. G. Martin, and D. Schifter (Eds.), *A research companion to principles and standards for school mathematics.* (pp. 250–262). Reston, VA: NCTM.

National Council of Teachers of Mathematics. (2000). *Principles and standards for school mathematics.* Reston, VA: Author.

National Council of Teachers of Mathematics. (2005). *Standards and curriculum: A view from the nation, a joint report by the National Council of Teachers of Mathematics (NCTM) and the Association of State Supervisors of Mathematics (ASSM).* J. W. Lott & K. Nishimura (Eds.). Reston, VA: Author.

National Governors Association Center/Council of Chief State School Officers (2010). Common Core State Standards for Mathematics. Retrieved from http://www.corestandards.org/the-standards/mathematics.

National Mathematics Advisory Panel. (2008). *Foundations for success: The final report of the National Mathematics Advisory Panel*. Washington, DC: U. S. Department of Education.

National Research Council. (2001). *Adding it up: Helping children learn mathematics*. J. Kilpatrick, J. Swafford, & B. Findell (Eds.). Washington, DC: National Academy Press.

Outhred, L., Mitchelmore, M., McPhail, D., & Gould, P. (2003). Count me into measurement: A program for the early elementary school. In D. H. Clements & G. Bright (Eds.). *Learning and teaching measurement: 2003 yearbook* (pp. 81–99). Reston, VA: NCTM.

Reed, D. S. (2009). Is there an expectations gap? Educational federalism and the demographic distribution of proficiency cut scores. *American Educational Research Journal, 46*(3), 718–742.

Reys, B. J., Chval, K., Dingman, S., McNaught, M., Regis, T. P., & Togashi, J. (2007). Grade-level learning expectations: A new challenge for elementary mathematics teachers. *Teaching Children Mathematics, 14*(1), 6–11.

Schneider, M. (2007). *National Assessment of Education Progress: Mapping 2005 state proficiency standards onto the NAEP scales*. Washington, DC: IES National Center for Education Statistics.

Sobel, M., & Maletsky, E. (1999). *Teaching mathematics: A sourcebook for aids, activities, and strategies* (3rd ed.). Boston, MA: Allyn & Bacon.

Van de Walle, J. A. (2004). *Elementary and middle school mathematics: Teaching developmentally* (5th ed.). Boston, MA: Pearson.

van Hiele, P. (1999). Developing geometric thinking through activities that begin with play. *Teaching Children Mathematics 5*(6), 310–316.

Index

A

About GO Math!, Program Overview, PG4–PG11

About the Math, In every Teacher Edition lesson. Some examples are: 49A, 175A, 245A, 265A, 297A, 317A, 351A, 357A, 421A, 439A, 451A, 491A, 617A

Building Mathematical Practices, 55A, 99A, 125A, 207A, 251A, 329A, 375A, 477A, 497A, 571A, 603A, 649A, 675A

If Students Ask, 11A, 37A, 61A, 277A, 335A, 383A, 511A

Teaching for Depth, 23A, 29A, 43A, 73A, 87A, 93A, 119A, 137A, 151A, 163A, 169A, 181A, 189A, 195A, 201A, 213A, 219A, 291A, 303A, 351A, 357A, 363A, 389A, 401A, 427A, 433A, 445A, 465A, 517A, 539A, 545A, 551A, 565A, 611A, 643A, 655A, 669A, 681A

Why Teach This?, 5A, 17A, 67A, 105A, 113A, 131A, 157A, 233A, 239A, 257A, 271A, 309A, 323A, 369A, 395A, 407A, 459A, 471A, 503A, 533A, 559A, 585A, 591A, 597A, 637A, 663A, 687A, 693A, 699A

Across the Grades, Common Core State Standards, 3J, 85J, 149J, 231J, 289J, 349J, 419J, 489H, 531J, 583J, 635J

Activities

Activity, 23, 371, 644, 650

Cross-Curricular. See Cross-Curricular Activities and Connections

Grab-and-Go!™. *See Grab-and-Go!*™ *Differentiated Centers Kit, In most Teacher Edition lessons. Some examples are:* 70, 216, 312, 474, 514, 672

Investigate, 5, 99, 151, 175, 181, 239, 265, 297, 317, 351, 357, 427, 439, 459, 491, 545, 663, 669, 675

Math in the Real World, 3, 85, 149, 231, 289, 349, 419, 489, 531, 583, 635

Mental Math, 17–20, 29–32, 219, 364, *407A,* 409, *597B,* 598

Response to Intervention (RtI).

RtI Tier I and *RtI Tier 2 Activities,* available online

RtI Tier 3 Activities. See Intensive Intervention.

Vocabulary Activity, 3H, 85H, 149H, 231H, 289H, 349H, 419H, 489F, 531H, 583H, 635H

Acute triangles, *643A–643B,* 643–646

Addition

Associative Property of, *17B,* 17–20, 219–222, *407A, 407B,* 407–410

Commutative Property of, *17B,* 17–20, 219–222, *407A, 407B,* 407–410

of decimals, 175–178, 195–198, 207–210, 219–222

estimation and, *189A, 189B,* 189–192, 195–198, 363–366

of fractions with unlike denominators, *349E, 351B,* 351–354, 375–378, 407–410

Identity Property of, 17–20

inverse operations with subtraction, 202, 401–403

of mixed numbers, *383A, 383B,* 383–386, 395–398, 401–404, 407–410

of money, 213–216

patterns, 207–210, 395–398

problem solving, 213–216, 401–404

properties of, 17–20, 219–222, 407–410

Advanced Learners, In every Teacher Edition lesson. Some examples are: 6, 126, 208, 330, 472, 676

Algebra

coordinate grid

plot ordered pairs, *531E,* 539–542, 551–554, 571–574

equations

addition, 17–20, 351–354, 401–404

division, 94, 517–520, 592, 623

multiplication, 17–20, 35, 94, 517, 591, 597

subtraction, 357–360, 401–404, 597

expressions, 17–20, 61–64, 67–70, 73–76

measurement

capacity, *583E,* 591–594, 611–614

conversions, 585–588, 591–594, 597–600, 603–606, 611–614, 617–620, 623–626

customary units, 585–588, 591–594, 597–600, 617–620

length, 585–588, 611–614

mass, 611–614

metric units, *583E, 583G, 611A, 611B,* 611–614, 617–620

multistep problems, 603–606

time, 623–626

weight, 597–600

patterns and relationships, 531E

patterns with decimals, 207–210, 233–236, 291–294

Progress to, PG29G–PG29H

Teacher Edition and Planning Guide references in *italics*; Planning Guide references begin with PG

H-diagram, 350

Health
Connect to Health, 32, 474

Heptagons, 637–640

Hexagonal prisms, 635, 655, 657

Hexagons, *637A, 637B,* 637–640, 655

HMH Mega Math, *In most Teacher Edition and Planning Guide lessons. Some examples are: 11A, 119A, 309A, 369A, 591A, 637A*

Hours, *623B,* 623–626

Identity Property of Addition, 17–20

Identity Property of Multiplication, 17–20, *445A,* 465

If Students Ask. *See About the Math*

Inches, 572–573, *585A, 585B,* 585–588, *603A*

Intensive Intervention, *3, 4, 85, 86, 149, 150, 231, 232, 289, 290, 349, 350, 419, 420, 489, 490, 531, 532, 583, 584, 635, 636*

Interpret the Remainder, *125A, 125B,* 125–128

Intervals, *551A, 551B,* 551–554

Intervention
Activities, Tier 1, available online for every lesson. See also Review Prerequisite Skills
Activities, Tier 2, available online for every lesson. See also Review Prerequisite Skills
Activities, Tier 3, 3, 4, 85, 86, 149, 150, 231, 232, 279, 289, 290, 349, 350, 420, 421, 489, 490, 531, 532, 583, 584, 635, 636. See also Review Prerequisite Skills
Assessment Intervention, PG14–PG15
Chapter at a Glance, 3A, 85A, 149A, 231A, 289A, 349A, 419A, 489A, 531A, 583A, 635A
Data-Driven Decision Making, In every Teacher Edition lesson. Some examples are: 35–36, 111–112, 315–316, 413–414, 629–630, 661–662
Diagnostic Assessment. See Assessment
Intensive Intervention, 3, 4, 85, 86, 149, 150, 231, 232, 289, 290, 349, 350, 419, 420, 489, 490, 531, 532, 583, 584, 635, 636

On-level Intervention, 4, 86, 150, 232, 290, 350, 420, 490, 532, 584, 636
Options, 4, 86, 150, 232, 290, 350, 420, 490, 532, 584, 636
Quick Check, In every Teacher Edition lesson. Some examples are: 159, 365, 499, 553, 587, 695
Reteach, In every Teacher Edition lesson. Some examples are: 5, 85, 283, 341, 557, 605
Review Prerequisite Skills, 3G, 85G, 149G, 231G, 289G, 349G, 419G, 489E, 531G, 583G, 635G
Show What You Know, 3, 85, 149, 231, 289, 349, 419, 489, 531, 583, 635
Strategic Intervention, 3, 4, 85, 86, 149, 150, 231, 232, 289, 290, 349, 350, 419, 420, 489, 490, 531, 532, 583, 584, 635, 636

Intervention Options, *4, 86, 150, 232, 290, 350, 420, 490, 532, 584, 636. See also Intervention*

Introduce the Project, *2, 348, 530*

Inverse operations
addition and subtraction, 202, 401–402
multiplication and division, *49B,* 49–52, 94–95, 491–494

Investigate, 5, 99, 151, 175, 181, 239, 265, 297, 317, 351, 357, 427, 439, 459, 491, 545, 663, 669, 675

Isosceles triangles, *637B, 643A–643B,* 643–646

iStudent Edition. *See Technology and Digital Resources*

iTools, *In some Teacher Edition lessons. Some examples are: 586, 593, 599, 612, 638*

Kilograms, 611–614

Kilometers, 611–614

Language Objective, *In every Teacher Edition lesson. Some examples are 5A, 151A, 351A, 491A, 533A, 637A. See also Chapter at a Glance*

Language Support. *See ELL Language Support*

Lateral faces, 655–658

Learning Objective, *In every Teacher Edition lesson. Some examples are: 5A, 151A, 351A, 491A, 533A, 637A*

Teacher Edition and Planning Guide references in *italics*; Planning Guide references begin with PG

Reading

Connect to Reading, 392, 588, 658

Developing Math Language, 3H, 85H, 149H, 231H, 289H, 349H, 419H, 489F, 531H, 583H, 635H

Literature, Grab-and-Go!™ Differentiated Centers Kit, In most Teacher Edition lessons. Some examples are: 70, 216, 312, 474, 672

Read the Problem, 55–56, 137–138, 213–214, 257–258, 335–336, 401–402, 477–478, 497–498, 565–566, 617–618, 693–694

Visualize It, 4, 86, 150, 232, 290, 350, 420, 490, 532, 584, 636

Real World

Unlock the Problem, In most lessons. Some examples are: 11, 29, 360, 401, 593, 699

Reasonableness, 93–96, 195–198, 201–204, 239, 247, 253, 258, 363–366, 369A, 375–378, 472, 480

Rectangles

properties of, *649A, 649B,* 649–652

Rectangular prisms,

properties of, 655–658

volume of, *635E,* 663–666, *669A, 669B,* 669–672, *675A, 675B,* 675–678, *681A, 681B,* 681–684, *687A, 687B,* 687–690, *693A, 693B,* 693–696, *699A, 699B,* 699–702

Rectangular pyramids

properties of, 655–658

References, Professional Development, PG108–PG109

Regrouping

decimal addition, *175A, 175B,* 175–178, *195A, 195B,* 195–198, *213B,* 213–216

decimal subtraction, *181A, 181B,* 181–184, *201A, 201B,* 201–204

division, 87–90, 93–96

multiplying, *37B,* 37–40, 43–46

Regular polygons, *637B,* 638–640

Relationships, mathematical

graphing, *571A, 571B,* 571–574

multiplication to division, *49A, 49B,* 49–52, 491–494

Remainders

in division, 88–90, 93–96

interpreting, *125A, 125B,* 125–128

writing as a fraction, 125–128

Remember, 12, 43, 88, 105, 189, 271, 291, 317, 364, 407

Renaming

fractions, 352, 389–392, 471

mixed numbers, 389–392, 471

Repeated reasoning, *561*

Resources. *See also* Technology and Digital Resources

Chapter at a Glance, *3A–3D, 85A–85D, 149A–149D, 231A–231D, 289A–289D, 349A–349D, 419A–419D, 489A–489B, 531A–531D, 583A–583D, 635A–635D*

End-of-Year Resources, *PG42–PG91*

Lesson at a Glance, In every Teacher Edition lesson. Some examples are: 5A, 151A, 351A, 491A, 533A, 637A

Planning Resources, PG30–PG37

Print Resources, 3A–3D, 85A–85D, 149A–149D, 231A–231D, 289A–289D, 349A–349D, 419A–419D, 489A–489B, 531A–531D, 583A–583D, 635A–635D

Response to Intervention (RtI).

RtI Tier 1 and *RtI Tier 2 Activities,* available online.

RtI Tier 3 Activities. See Intensive Intervention.

Reteach, *In every Teacher Edition lesson. Some examples are: 5, 85, 283, 341, 557, 605*

Reteach Activities. *See also Differentiated Instruction*

RtI Tier 1, available online for every lesson

Review Projects, *PG42–PG47*

Review and Test. *See also* Assessment

Accessing Prior Knowledge, 3, 85, 149, 231, 289, 349, 419, 489, 531, 583, 635

Chapter at a Glance, 3A–3D, 85A–85D, 149A–149D, 231A–231D, 289A–289D, 349A–349D, 419A–419D, 489A–489D, 531A–531D, 583A–583D, 635A–635D

Chapter Review/Test, 79–84, 143–148, 225–230, 283–288, 341–346, 413–418, 483–488, 523–528, 577–582, 629–634, 705–710

Chapter Test, 84A–84B, 148A–148B, 230A–230B, 288A–288B, 346A–346B, 418A–418B, 488A–488B, 528A–528B, 582A–582B, 634A–634B, 710A–710B

Mid-Chapter Checkpoint, 35–36, 111–112, 187–188, 263–264, 315–316, 381–382, 457–458, 509–510, 557–558, 609–610, 661–662

Problem of the Day, In every Teacher Edition lesson. Some examples are: 43B, 131B, 219B, 309B, 427B, 565B

Quick Check, In every Teacher Edition lesson. Some examples are: 159, 365, 499, 553, 587, 695

Review Prerequisite Skills, 3I, 85I, 149I, 231I, 289I, 349I, 419I, 489G, 531I, 583I, 635I

Review Projects, PG42–PG47

Review Words, 4, 86, 150, 232, 290, 350, 420, 490, 532, 584, 636

Show What You Know, 3, 85, 149, 231, 289, 349, 419, 489, 531, 583, 635

Teacher Edition and Planning Guide references in *italics***; Planning Guide references begin with PG**